Donated by

Warren Kump M.D.

THE STORY OF THE JOHNS HOPKINS

Dr. Bernheim *is Associate Professor (Emeritus) of Surgery, the Johns Hopkins Medical School; Surgeon to the Johns Hopkins Hospital*

The Four Physicians

From the painting by Sir John Singer Sargent

The Story of the
JOHNS HOPKINS

*Four Great Doctors and
the Medical School They Created*

by

Bertram M. Bernheim, M.D.

WHITTLESEY HOUSE
McGraw-Hill Book Company, Inc.
New York : Toronto

THE STORY OF THE JOHNS HOPKINS

Copyright, 1948, *by* BERTRAM M. BERNHEIM

PUBLISHED BY WHITTLESEY HOUSE

A DIVISION OF THE McGRAW-HILL BOOK COMPANY, INC.

PRINTED IN THE UNITED STATES OF AMERICA

To

H. M. B.

This Book

WHAT I SET OUT TO DO AND HOW
I HOPE YOU WILL REGARD IT

IN THE Navy they talk of a "happy ship." I have never heard a similar designation applied to universities but it well might be. There is also another adjective: lucky. I think the Johns Hopkins has been a lucky institution and, generally speaking, a happy one.

Essentially I have tried to tell a human interest story—with historical connotations. It is the story of a great experiment—the founding in America of an institution for higher education in medicine. I feel totally inadequate to deal with the Johns Hopkins from the purely historical standpoint and I can't even attempt a recitation and evaluation of its manifold scientific achievements.

I do feel qualified, however, to deal with it from the general and human interest angles because it happens that I came upon the scene not so very long after the experiment got under way—A.B., 1901; M.D., 1905—and boy and man, undergraduate, medical student, doctor and staff member, I have watched it unfolding for fifty years. Not only that, I had acquaintance with practically all the chief actors in the play. One thing, though, I would make clear. I was never one of the important men at Hopkins, a member of the inner circle. My status was merely that of member of that large group you find in all institutions who carry out orders and keep things going. You rarely hear of them, but they are important. Because they have no responsibility for success or failure they can always do things better!

There was always color and flavor at the Hopkins. From the very start things were different and there was an air of culture, refinement, and appreciation of the finer things that you found nowhere else in the realm of American medicine—to the same degree. I wish to convey some of this to you, for therein lies much of the message the great figures who laid the foundations gave to posterity. To do this I have been at pains to paint true likenesses of the chief actors, sketching in their backgrounds, the forces at work around them, the times in which they lived, together with the scientific, practical, and social implications as they appeared to me. I have also endeavored to describe the unfolding of the pattern that was to change the Hopkins from its beginning as a simple medical school and inadequate hospital to an all-embracing medical center of many great clinics, schools, and institutes—without going into the detailed recitation of each addition's inner workings. I hope especially that you will bear this latter in mind, since it is the chronological development and the fact of new specialties being added that is most important to this work. It would take me too far afield, besides being tiresome for you, to do otherwise, and those who wish to know details are respectfully referred to the proper authorities.

I have made conscious effort to take the objective viewpoint but have not hesitated to explain, evaluate, take some slight license in order to round out the story, give opinion, enter into the picture, and even criticize when I thought it advisable. I have not consulted, to any degree, my colleagues, and no one of them has seen this manuscript. No official of the Hopkins has, either. The work is not inspired propaganda. The few men to whom I went for assistance were those in position to give reliable information concerning the scientific and practical aims of special clinics with which I was not entirely familiar. Naturally they had to know what I was up to and naturally they were interested, but such discussions as we had of the over-all picture of the Hopkins were only in passing.

At first glance this may seem strange to you and some will attribute it to sheer and unadulterated egotism. I can only say that composite pictures never appealed to me because they cannot be sharply drawn. Right or wrong, I accept full responsibility for the views and opinions herein expressed—without in any sense claiming that they are correct or representative of general staff thought.

For the rest, I would only say that it wasn't all books and bones and cure-alls at the Hopkins, or all science and laboratories, with stuffy men and stuffier lectures. There was a creative, inspired genius over all, and no little of high drama.

BERTRAM M. BERNHEIM

CONTENTS

THIS BOOK. What I Set Out to Do and How I Hope You Will
Regard It   vii

PROLOGUE   xi

CHAPTER

1. Mr. Johns Hopkins—Enigma   1
2. Four Great Doctors and an Aura   7
3. Doctor-Actors   18
4. Baltimore. Admission of Women to the Hopkins   26
5. Hopkins and the University of Maryland. Dispensary
   Work. Evenings at Osler's Home   35
6. The Resident System   43
7. Cordiality Between Scientific and Clinical Sides. Anatomy
   and Mall   53
8. Physiology and Pharmacology. Doctors Abel and Howell   60
9. Five Distinctive Features   70
10. Osler Leaves. Osler and Welch   76
11. Harvey Cushing and the Hunterian Laboratory   85
12. Walter Dandy, Neurosurgeon   99
13. Phipps Psychiatric Clinic   102
14. Pediatric Clinic   107
15. Hugh Young and the Brady Urological Institute   111
16. School of Hygiene and Public Health   118
17. Obstetrics. J. Whitridge Williams   122
18. F. H. Baetjer—Martyr to Science   128
19. Max Brödel. Johns Hopkins and the Magic Formula   131
20. Supreme Court for Diagnosis. Americana. The Hopkins
    and the Mayo Clinic   135
21. Hopkins Policy with Regard to Its Clinical Men. Five
    Sitting Ducks and a Secondary Medical Center   142
22. John M. T. Finney. Halsted and Finney   153
23. Hopkins Jumps the Gun on Full Time. World War I   163
24. Wilmer Eye Clinic   170

x Contents

CHAPTER
25. Welch Institute of the History of Medicine   172
26. Love and Rubber Gloves. Hopkins Nurses   177
27. The Hopkins Between Wars. Deterioration? Mistakes?   183
28. The Hopkins Medical Graduate. Consideration of Objec-
      tives   192
29. World War II. Hopkins Points to Complete Full Time   202
30. They've Got Youth. Will History Repeat Itself? The New
      and Bigger Hopkins. Tomorrow's Medicine. Conclusion   210
APPENDIX   221
BIBLIOGRAPHY   225
INDEX   227

The Hopkins

PROLOGUE

ONE EVENING not so very long ago my wife and I stood alongside our train waiting for a red-cap. It was early spring and Baltimore's damp, chilly air was a terrible let-down from Florida's warm, seductive sunshine. Most of the passengers had departed but among the few stragglers there appeared the drabbest, poorest looking old couple I'd almost ever seen. Slowly, almost painfully making their way along the brick platform they came to the bottom of the long stairway leading to the station's main waiting room, looked up it, hesitated a moment, and stopped. The woman, excessively slender, pale, wearing a very thin greenish coat that had seen much better days, was holding on to the man's left arm looking rather dazed. The man, bent, very thin, face pinched, scraggly, colorless mustache, handkerchief that was once white draped about his lower face, edge at the lip, blinked at the lights, lifted his crooked homemade walking stick as if about to take another step, but didn't. Turning to the train conductor who was standing nearby he said in a thin, husky voice:

"Them steps the way to git out?"

"Yes, sir. Go right on up and turn to your right."

The couple slowly started up and then stopped. Turning back to the conductor the man said:

"I'm going to the hospital." Whereupon he seemed satisfied and went on his way.

The conductor just nodded. "They're going to Johns Hopkins," he said to me—and he, too, seemed satisfied.

Chapter 1

MR. JOHNS HOPKINS—ENIGMA

IF YOU are a doctor in these United States, you have been affected by the Johns Hopkins Medical School and Hospital.

This is a big, broad, bold statement—some will say it is typical of the Hopkins ego—but when you consider that the Hopkins first proposed graduate education in American medicine and forthwith proceeded to carry it out in every detail and according to plan, its truth cannot be denied.

You will note the words "according to plan." The Hopkins did not just happen. Unlike other institutions of medicine in our country it did not just grow and develop. It was definitely planned; money adequate for all purposes—land, buildings, equipment, men —was provided in advance, and so was the basic idea. It was Americana at its best and in every detail. Johns Hopkins, a country boy of seventeen, went out into the world, amassed a great fortune, and founded a university. Crusty old bachelor, financial genius, shrewd man of business, this is the last thing you would have expected him to do—especially the provision for a hospital and medical school— but Johns Hopkins presents something of an enigma.

Of all the many early personages associated with the University we know least about him. Volumes have been written about Gilman, Remsen, Rowland, Gildersleeve, Welch, Osler, Halsted, and all the others, but Johns Hopkins, the man, the founder, stands in a class by himself—alone, aloof, inscrutable. He has no saga, or, at best, a pathetic thing that does him scant justice and makes little sense. This man who had the vision to plan and lay out the specifications for a great institute of learning must have been something more than the disagreeable, vindictive old fellow contemporary history pictures.

A poor boy got pushed around; made good; got tough with people and the society that did the pushing—and became thoroughly disliked. That about sums up the story of Mr. Johns Hopkins as we get it, and the dislike was so thorough that the people of his time

1

couldn't even forgive him or overlook things when he finally came through with the most magnificent gift a community had ever received. On the contrary, it seemed to enrage them still further, and they couldn't say enough bad things about him. He was a miser; he drank; he mulcted the lowly of their savings, even of their property. Thus he came by great real estate holdings and warehouses which he rented out at exorbitant prices—and never improved or sold! Truly, Mr. Hopkins was a man to be shunned, and parents passed the word on to their children, who kept alive the cant of the old so-and-so's badness.

In short, the citizenry of Baltimore did not seem to like Mr. Johns Hopkins and made no secret of it. You'd have thought he came from across the railroad tracks, the way they acted, but he hadn't. He came from good but humble British stock—Church of England, but later on Friends. It was from his great-great-grandfather, Richard Johns, that he received his Christian name, and that is of interest because Johns is certainly an unusual one. He was born May 19, 1795, on a tobacco plantation in Anne Arundel County, Maryland, halfway between Baltimore and Annapolis, and his father and mother were Samuel and Hannah Hopkins. There were eleven children in all—six sons, of whom Johns was the second, and five daughters. The Hopkinses were people of means and lived well until Johns was about twelve years old, at which time his father freed all his slaves. It was a sort of humanitarian and religious gesture and followed weeks and months of soul-searching. This was in 1807, long before the Civil War of course, but the Quakers were people who looked things straight in the eye and formed their own conclusions. The Society of Friends decreed that all were to free their slaves, without compensation of any sort, or be put out of meeting.

Without their slaves the Hopkins family didn't have sufficient labor to farm their plantation in the usual manner, and so bad times resulted. Thus it happened that young Johns was needed on the farm and had to give up schooling while still a youth. He was a blue-eyed, long-legged boy with an eager, intelligent face, and though he had been much interested in history and English literature and other things, he dutifully went to the aid of his parents.

Prosperity did not attend the Hopkins family, though, and when Johns was seventeen his mother told him not to stay on the plantation any longer. She is reported to have said, "Thee has business ability and thee must go where the money is." Accordingly, he left the old homestead—it was called Whitehall—and went to Baltimore to live with his uncle, Gerard Hopkins. This latter event was a cornerstone in Johns Hopkins's life and, curiously enough, from two different angles. The one was love, the other was business. Gerard Hopkins had a daughter, Elizabeth, and Johns fell in love with her. They wanted to marry, but Uncle Gerard objected strenuously to an alliance between cousins and forbade it. This was some seven years after the boy had come to Baltimore, and it was following that that he left his uncle's house. It is interesting that neither Elizabeth Hopkins nor Johns Hopkins ever married. Elizabeth lived to the ripe old age of eighty-five and died in a house that Johns had given her. They remained friends throughout their lives.

Naturally, young Johns was bitter toward his uncle, but that did not appear to be the reason for his leaving the business. His uncle had a prosperous wholesale grocery business and had taken his nephew in with him, but he was quite a religious man and spent too much of his time going around the country preaching at the Friends' meetinghouses. At least Johns thought he did, and following the unfortunate ending of his love affair made no bones about it. Moreover, his uncle had business scruples that Johns didn't like. It seems that some of the customers of his provision house who lived in Virginia and North Carolina couldn't pay for their goods in money and wished to pay in kind, part of the kind being whisky. The elder Hopkins wouldn't permit this, and so there finally came a break. From all accounts, Johns Hopkins had shown keen business ability from the very start and when he finally withdrew from his uncle's business he took several of his brothers in with him and formed a wholesale provision house of his own. It was known as Hopkins Brothers and prospered from the beginning. They took whisky in payment for goods and sold it under the brand of "Hopkins Best." Just how much of a whisky business Hopkins did is not revealed but it may have been considerable because he was in it for some years. As a matter of fact, this whisky business offended the Society of Friends, and he was temporarily turned out of the meeting. He continued to sell the whisky, nevertheless, but he also continued to contribute to the Society and went regularly to their meetings and was later on reinstated. In his later life he is said to have regretted having been in the whisky business and told his nephew Joseph Hopkins, that it was wrong and that he looked upon it as the greatest mistake of his life. One is permitted to have his own opinion about this. Lots of wealthy men later in life "get religion," as it were, but the fact remains that the things they did earlier in life to greater or lesser extent were the foundations of their prosperity, and they might not have been so great if they had not done as they did.

However the case may be, Johns Hopkins became a very wealthy man and was able to branch out into other endeavors. One of these was banking and another was railroading; at least railroading to the extent of his becoming heavily interested in the new and growing Baltimore and Ohio Railroad. He became a director in 1847, and in 1855 was elected chairman of the finance committee and became a real power. He is said to have owned between fifteen and seventeen thousand shares of the railroad's stock, and in the panics of 1857 and 1873 he pledged his private fortune and endorsed notes for the railroad to the amount of $1,000,000 in order to save it. He was chairman of its finance committee to the time of his death and it was after his death that the railroad came to grief financially. I make this point now because his interest in the B. & O. Railroad had tremendous implications for the Hopkins University later on.

From all I can gather, Johns Hopkins was a shrewd business man who knew what he wanted and got it. It was said that people either loved or hated him, but the lovers seem to have been definitely in the minority. At that, there may have been a tinge of jealousy in the animosity displayed toward him because of the power and influence he wielded. Baltimore was then, as it is to this day, rather provincial in its social attitudes, and one could not miss the impression that the city's upper group regarded Mr. Johns Hopkins as something of an upstart and a man of little culture. He seems to have survived the low esteem in which he was held, but we get the impression that he was a lonely, unhappy man who lived mostly within himself. He did have relatives close by, and some of his nieces and nephews and their children visited him in his palatial home on the outskirts of the city, but there was always restraint and a sort of enforced gaiety, if gaiety there was. Dinners and functions were formal and the old gentleman was irascible of temper, sharp of tongue, and not too liberal in the little gifts that mean so much to the young.

In a little book called *A Silhouette*, Helen Hopkins Thom, great-grandniece, tries to soften the picture of Johns Hopkins, but the effort is too palpable to fool anyone. In fact, the only thing of real worth in the book is the introductory note by John C. French, then (1929) librarian of the Johns Hopkins University. "The materials for a life of Johns Hopkins," says Mr. French, "are necessarily scanty. He was a merchant and a banker, not a man of public affairs nor in any sense a man of letters. He left, therefore, no voluminous journal, no public speeches, no literary letters composed with the consciousness that posterity was looking over his shoulder. It is only by a fortunate chance that the story of his apprenticeship in his uncle's store and the circumstances which gave loose rein to his genius for business has been preserved in reminiscences which he gave to a relative."

How a man of Johns Hopkins's character, temperament, education, and background came to found an institution that was later to become world-renowned is a question, and so far as I have been able to discover there is no adequate explanation. As noted, he was not a man of great education, he was not a student, and he had not been much of a traveler. Obviously, though, he must have had many contacts and, being a brainy man, he probably made the most of them. It has been suggested that certain men might have influenced him—George Peabody is one—but nothing was proved, and it would be my feeling that he did his own thinking—possibly aided and abetted by his erstwhile love and lifelong friend, Elizabeth.

Stranger things have happened, and the early attachment of the two Hopkins cousins cannot be lightly tossed aside. Elizabeth was a lovely girl and had strength of character, besides being well educated. It does not require too great a stretch of the imagination to believe that she bitterly regretted her decision to abide by her father's wishes and refuse marriage to Johns. Too proud to admit it and seek the union later on, yet seeing better than others the great potentialities of the man and understanding him, what could be more natural than that she found ways and means to soften the blow he had received and mold his character to her way of thinking?

Johns Hopkins was a man of strong will and great determination. He had a mind of his own. His chief pleasure, his chief outlet, was making money. Once he made it there came the question of usage. It needed only the seed of the University idea to set his mind to working. Elizabeth might well have sowed that seed. Johns did the rest.

Chapter 2

FOUR GREAT DOCTORS AND AN AURA

Four doctors of superior talents and unique personalities made the medical side of Johns Hopkins University great and they created an aura of glamour and excellence that has persisted ever since. They became "The Four Physicians" who have been immortalized in the painting by Sir John Singer Sargent, known the world over and now reposing in the great hall of the Welch Memorial Library Building at Hopkins.

Welch, Osler, Halsted, and Kelly became "The Four Saints" really, and the story of the early Hopkins is chiefly their story—collectively and indivisibly. They weave in and out of it so constantly, and their lives and work are so closely associated, that it would dull the intent of this work if the usual orthodox custom of giving individual life stories were to be followed in their cases. It will suffice for the present merely to say that William H. Welch, born in 1850, was of New England origin; William S. Halsted, who was born in the year 1852, was from New York City; William Osler, born in 1849, was a Canadian; and Howard Kelly was born in New Jersey in 1858. Welch and Halsted were both educated at Yale and Columbia Universities, Osler at McGill in Montreal, and Kelly at Pennsylvania. The first three men apparently came from rather more distinguished ancestry than Kelly and had more formal education. Not that the one or the other necessarily had any bearing on their subsequent courses, or the story, but they may have. I rather think they did. Kelly was more of the practical man than the other three and though equally individualistic he was different in a subtle but nonetheless definite sort of way. For example, he was the only one of the four who ever made any real money, yet he was anything but materialistic and much less the man of the world than his mates.

Clubs and dinners, and the social world with its good cheer and big and little talk hadn't the slightest lure for Kelly, but they did for the others. Various religious and altruistic affairs occupied much

7

of Kelly's attention. At one time he achieved notoriety as a vice crusader. He was a collector of reptiles. Money was mostly a by-product of his professional ability to be scattered among his interests. He did, however, have a big family of nine children and, of course, it took money to provide for them. There was only one child among the other three doctors (Dr. Welch never married). Osler's son, Revere, was killed in World War I. He was not a doctor, and only one of Kelly's children studied medicine.

You can thus see, I think, that the story of the Four Physicians at the Hopkins can only come alive through the unorthodox method of group handling—with the occasional digression necessitated by special circumstances. Other less important figures, whose scope was more circumscribed, lend themselves to orthodoxy and will be so handled, but not the Four. They were in a class by themselves.

All four physicians were present at the birth of the Hopkins (1889, capacity 220 beds) and a new era in American medical education dawned. Actually, Welch was a bit beforehand. Pathologist, physician, surgeon, gynecologist, the Four took the new infant to themselves and literally swept it to maturity and first rank without so much as a gesture to the usual childhood years. Working as a team, but individualists just the same, they plotted new courses and followed through with a judgment and a verve and an enthusiasm that made them preeminent in American medicine almost overnight. They had spirit, they had humanity, they had knowledge and deep understanding of illness, disease, and people. Especially did they understand people, and their sympathy knew no bounds. Yet they didn't stand around and wring their hands and cry their eyes out over the sufferings they saw and the woe they had to deal with.

It was by fortuitous circumstance that they came to the Hopkins at one and the same time, at the psychological moment. A break; a quirk of fate. Any one of them would have brought renown, but together they brought fame. For they were the spirit and they were inspired, and theirs was a God-given quality that you see once in a great while when the need is great and the time is ripe. Welch, Osler, Halsted, Kelly were naturals for the Hopkins Medical Department. They were more than doctors; they were men; they were teachers; they were executives, organizers, compilers, lecturers, research workers, writers, advisers—even actors and propagandists, though they probably didn't realize that.

Do you say I am being extravagant? Of course I am. They were extravagant men. They'd have done well in any walk of life—industry, finance, politics. They'd have taken over because they had what it takes—individually and collectively. I haven't the slightest doubt they'd have made a night club of Alcatraz if by some strange fate they had been sent there and had wanted to. Men just naturally flocked to them—doctors, students, the sick, the lowly, the big rich, gamblers, men, women, and children. All gave them their confidence; all hung on their words; all took their advice; all went their ways happy and believing.

They comprised the most extraordinary group the world of medicine ever saw or probably ever will see. And that in a nutshell spells the fame of the Johns Hopkins Hospital and Medical School. It spells the fame in great measure, too, of Daniel C. Gilman,* President of the Hopkins, and John Shaw Billings, army doctor and famed organizer and planner of hospitals—lent to the Board of Directors of Hopkins when they set out to build the new medical institution. Gilman and Billings sweated out the erection of the Hospital and Medical School and they were the chief selectors of the first staff. Both of them could have signed off the day they chose Welch to be Professor of Pathology, just as the original Board of Directors could have signed off the day they chose Gilman to be first President of the University.

For Gilman was smart and he'd had long training in educational and executive matters at Yale and elsewhere. Despite the fact that he had started out as a physical geographer, he got switched into these other channels in which he had superlative talents, and the Hopkins Board of Directors somehow got hold of him and turned him loose. I don't say that they didn't aid him in organizing and setting in motion the Philosophical Faculty and Graduate School

* Flexner, Abraham, *Daniel Coit Gilman: Creator of the American Type of University*, Harcourt, Brace & Company, Inc., New York, 1947.

of the Johns Hopkins University proper—1876—or that its instant
and phenomenal success wasn't due in part to their efforts, but Gilman was the works. There always has to be some one man who is
the brain if you're going to go places. Boards and committees, composed as they are of part-time nonprofessionals, never accomplish
anything on their own. All they can do is investigate and advise
and counsel, and if they are men of parts like the early Hopkins
trustees were, they can render valuable assistance.

But there always has to be the master mind, and at Johns Hopkins that was Gilman. He had the know-how. He understood that
it was a different kind of university they were starting in Baltimore—a university for the higher education of special students who
had been specially prepared. There was to be nothing of the little
five-by-five stuff or the rah-rah college about the Hopkins. It was
to be *work* of the highest possible character; it was to be all study;
it was to be science and investigation—for staff and students alike.
Gilman was enthusiastic and he gathered a faculty equally enthusiastic and imbued with the same ideas. Little wonder the Hopkins
enrolled students of high caliber immediately and from all corners
of the land. Little wonder the fame and notoriety of its men and
their accomplishments projected the new school of learning into
first place among American universities.

And then came the Medical Department. It had always been in
the offing—with the money provided, and the basic idea of graduate
education like the original school. They began the preliminary work
of investigation and planning for the plant years before the building of it got under way. They also did some initial scouting for
possible staff material, and that's how they came up with Welch.
Billings found him working in a laboratory in Leipzig with Ludwig.
That was in 1876, and the two talked of the experiment in medical
education presently to be inaugurated at the Hopkins. Welch was
impressed, but the thing was still in embryo, and he went on with
his studies. Later on he worked in Cohnheim's laboratory for
pathology and research in Breslau, and it was this same Cohnheim
who tipped off Gilman to him.

As I have said, Gilman could have signed off the day he signed on William H. Welch. I don't say he didn't do yeoman service in getting the Hospital under way—he was, in fact, its first director, though only for about a year. Henry M. Hurd, who so ably and so long—1889 to 1911—directed the fortunes of the Hospital, is generally regarded as its first superintendent. But just as Gilman was the works in the University proper, so Welch became the works in the Hospital and Medical School. It was a remarkable contrast: Gilman, physical geographer, became a power in graduate education; Welch, a pathologist, became a power in medical education. He became the first medical statesman in America, perhaps the only one the nation has ever seen—and it all redounded to the credit of the Hopkins.

A little, rotund, bald-headed man with a twinkle in his eye, a pleasant smile and a soft voice, an easy, lucid speaker, he immediately took the helm at the Hopkins Hospital and Medical School and till the day of his death, many years later, held it. He backed Halsted for surgery and he had a hand in getting Osler. Osler, in turn, got Kelly. All four men were in their thirties, Kelly being the youngest. He was thirty-one, the others six or seven years older. Osler was a Canadian but came to the Hopkins from the University of Pennsylvania, and so did Kelly. They had been Professor of Medicine and of Obstetrics, respectively. Welch and Halsted came from New York, where both had done some private practice; Welch, believe it or not, in medicine and obstetrics, Halsted in surgery. Neither man had been much interested in private practice, though, and when Welch got his call to come to Baltimore he was running a pathological laboratory in connection with the Bellevue Hospital Medical College. It was a little, inadequately financed thing, but already men had begun to take notice of the young doctor and were regularly attending his courses.

There was plenty of drama connected with the development of the Hopkins, some of it intense. Halsted, for instance, didn't come to the Hopkins as a surgeon at all; he came originally as a friend of Dr. Welch—to work in Welch's laboratory. As noted, he had been engaged in practice in New York City but had also been doing some research work in anesthesia, notably cocaine anesthesia. He and three other young doctors had been working together in this and they were so enthusiastic that they experimented on themselves. This isn't at all unusual among research workers, but the young doctors didn't know how insidiously deadly the thing they were dealing with was and so before they knew what it was all about they all became cocaine addicts. It is said that the other three went the usual way of cocaine addicts and died miserable deaths, but Welch saved Halsted by taking him away and putting him in various sanatoria. Therefore, when Welch, in 1885, came to the Hopkins, he very soon had Halsted join him. It isn't clear what his purpose was; that is, whether he then had him in mind for the Professorship of Surgery, but that could have been the case. He knew Halsted's ability and he knew that Halsted had done good research work, but of course he couldn't be sure how his young friend would turn out, that is, whether he had really been cured of his affliction. So for a year or so Halsted worked in Welch's laboratory doing pathology and research work while Welch kept his keen eye on him. Once Welch became convinced that Halsted was cured he backed him for a job in the Surgical Department of the new Hospital at the time of its opening and he got Osler to help him. This was in 1889, and Osler gave the Board of Directors his opinion that Halsted was all right.

The Board didn't give Halsted the Chair of Surgery but they did make him associate professor. There was some hesitancy even in giving him this, because they had been informed of his affliction and, of course, they had felt that he ought to be watched. When at the end of a year they became convinced that a cure had been effected, they then made him Professor, and he held the chair until his death.

It would appear that the Board of Directors, and possibly President Gilman, had some idea that the key departments in the new Hospital, medicine and surgery, ought to be in the hands of better known, more mature men. I dare say they were a little nervous and felt that if they had some big names connected with the new institution it would go over better with the doctors and students and the general public. Sir Thomas Lauder Brunton, famed London physician, was one of the men they considered for the Chair of Medicine, and Sir William Macewen of Glasgow was approached for the Chair of Surgery. Neither man accepted, and it was after that that the positions were given to Osler and Halsted. I wouldn't be surprised, though, if it was Dr. Welch who persuaded the Board away from their early idea, because he had been on the scene for several years before the hospital opened in 1889. It is more than likely that they were already leaning heavily on him, and when their first choices refused, they decided to take his advice and call in Osler and Halsted. This was a fortunate circumstance because if they hadn't done that it is unlikely that Dr. Kelly would have come to the Department of Gynecology, and they would have lost a perfect dynamo of energy and a man of great originality. Welch once said that Kelly spread the fame of the University to the remote corners of the world by his ingenious operations and his development of instruments, doing much more for the University even than he, Osler, or Halsted had. I would doubt this, but it goes to show that Kelly was very highly regarded by his other teammates. However the case may be, I would also doubt whether older, more mature men could have brought the Hopkins to the forefront either so rapidly or so well as did the younger men that were finally put in charge. There wouldn't have been the teamwork, and there wouldn't have been the spirit and the originality. Older men who have made their marks elsewhere and are entrenched don't usually risk much and so are content to introduce into any new fields to which they may be called their old ideas, many of which may have been outworn. I would, however, think that Welch still would eventually have gotten control and maintained it, and I would think, too, that sooner or later he would have supplanted the older men by newer men, but by that time Osler, Halsted, and Kelly probably would have been beyond reach.

So the Hopkins had a backfield for its prospective football team, and with Welch at quarterback calling the signals there was no question of its performing great feats. Graduate doctors had begun to come and sit at the feet of Welch several years before the Hospital opened its doors, and in that way and through the travels of

Gilman and Billings, and through press notices, news of the great Johns Hopkins experiment in medical education got abroad and made itself felt. It was to be a postgraduate school, and prospective students were not only to have college degrees, they were to have taken certain prescribed courses of a preparatory nature—so-called premedical course.

This was so different from the usual thing in American medicine, and the standards set were so high that there was doubt of getting students. It was perhaps a fortunate circumstance, therefore, that there was delay in opening the Medical School. Financial troubles in the original Hopkins Baltimore and Ohio Railroad holdings were responsible, and it wasn't until 1893, four years after the Hospital was opened, that the school opened its doors for business. At that time twenty students qualified (fifteen graduated) and from then on there was never any doubt of the school's appeal. Each year saw more and more applicants, and it finally ended up in enrollment being limited to seventy-five in each class. The first class ever graduated was in 1897, and more than one member of that group became famous in his own right.

But it was not only students who began flocking to the new institution. It was young scientists and surgeons and physicians as well—men who had learned of the great experiment, men who were hearing great things, unusual things, about the Four Galloping Horsemen who were placing the Hopkins on the map. They wanted to be associated with them; they wanted to be their house officers and assistants. They wanted to get in on the ground floor of the new experiment and have a share in it. And they were willing and ready to risk their all.

It was really a most extraordinary movement, this trek of young up-and-coming doctors to the Hopkins—all due chiefly to the lure and the spell of the great actors, Welch, Osler, Halsted, and Kelly. Whether it was in anatomy or pharmacology or physiology or medicine or surgery, men grasped at the opportunity to join up; and that is how Mall and Abel and Howell and Flexner and Councilman, just to mention a few stalwarts, came to cast in their lot. Fantastic, you'd almost call it, the way they came—and were developed. Later

on, when the school began turning out its own men, there wasn't so
much room for outsiders, but certain numbers have continued to
be welcomed, if only to introduce new blood.

Perhaps I should tell you that I knew most of these men—even
President Gilman—and thus it happens that much of the stuff I
am giving you is firsthand. I came to Baltimore in the fall of 1897
to enter the undergraduate school, and it was there that I saw
Dr. Gilman and heard him speak and even had one or two little
conversations with him. He was already in his heyday, and I recall
that he was pleasant and genial, albeit, to me, a bit on the stuffy,
pompous side. Rather a tall man, with a fine face—high forehead,
sideburns—always immaculately dressed, he didn't know how to
unbend to boys and talk their language but he wanted to, and we
knew or took for granted he was a great man. It was the same with
Gildersleeve, Greek scholar, and Remsen, renowned chemist, and
Rowland, physicist extraordinary, and Joe Ames, later President,
and most of the others. They seemed mostly to have their heads in
the clouds and to be weighed down with problems. The whole atmosphere of the place—it was then in the heart of the city—was
lugubrious, and graduate and undergraduate departments were piled
on top of each other in quarters that were too cramped. I was an
immature boy from the Middle West and not too understanding.
I didn't like it at all and felt sure none of the men who taught me
knew much of the world. I didn't think they were interested in
what was going on or ever had a good time. Those were the days
when the Baltimore Orioles were making baseball history, and it
would have been dollars to doughnuts that those Hopkins men,
from Gilman down, had never heard of Mugsy McGraw or Robin-
son or Wee Willie Keeler, who made the famous remark that if
you're going to be a batter you've got to "hit 'em where they ain't."
Poor men, what they missed! Perhaps I should say that Yale had
been my choice for college, but Abraham Flexner had influenced
my father, and those were the days when boys did as they were told.

It was different when I finally went to the Medical School. The
atmosphere there was less heavy, less oppressive, even though it
was plain to be seen that they all meant business. I don't think the

doctors knew much about the Orioles, either, but they did about the goings on of college football, and when Yale played Harvard or Harvard played Princeton, the Hospital and Medical School practically closed down because so many of the staff found themselves suddenly and unaccountably called out of the city! That proved, of course, that they were human, which was more than you could say of the group across town. I take it you know that the University is on one side of the city and the Hospital and Medical School are on the other—a little matter that will be explained shortly.

What impressed me most, though, was the spirit and the general good will of the medical side. They all seemed to be friends and they loved to help each other. They used to visit and talk and sit around over sandwiches and pretzels and a glass of beer at the little corner saloon—Louie Hanselman's place. (Even Welch and Halsted and Osler, so it is said. Never Kelly. He was a teetotaler.) Most of the time they'd be working or attending lectures or clinics or autopsies or medical meetings. There was a charming informality and the talk was good—talk of all kinds: politics, books, the theater, music, but mostly medicine and research. Nobody seemed to be in a hurry. You went to your classes regularly, and nobody skipped or cut out. Yet there was no roll call, and nobody seemed to bother whether you came or went. Moreover, it seemed to be fun, this instruction that they were giving you, and not too difficult. Leastways not all of it. I had a terrible time with chemistry and pharmacology and anatomy but somehow got by.

Dr. Welch was the first of the Four Horsemen we met, because pathology came in the second year. This isn't to say that the men we got in the first year were small fry—not Howell and Abel and Mall! But they weren't "Popsy." Dr. Welch became familiarly known throughout the land by that appellation, and it used to be said that "nobody knew where Popsy ate; nobody knew where Popsy slept." He was so much on the go and occupied with so many and varied projects even by the time my class came along—and we were only the ninth graduating class (1905)—the great man was finding it more and more difficult to keep his lecture appointments. He'd usually come hurrying into the room, talking as he walked up the aisle—and never from notes. If he was very late, one or the other of his assistants would begin, but if he got there at all, he took over and went on. I remember once when he came back from Europe full up with Metchnikoff's new side-chain theory of bacterial growth. He just stepped up to the blackboard, took a piece of chalk, and forthwith launched into the most abstruse disquisition imaginable, drawing all kinds of weird-looking things—and never using a note. It was fascinating to watch him and listen to the easy, continuous flow of words even if you didn't understand a thing he was talking about—as I didn't. And then when an hour or so later he was finished and seemed so pleased with himself, who were we to object?

There were other times, however, when Popsy did come down to our level, and there were medical meetings and pathological conferences and just little gatherings where he stood or sat and talked. The crowd always grew, and the delight everyone took in listening to this man was only too obvious. There was nothing he didn't know, no book he hadn't read, no research he hadn't a hand in. They even said he read the encyclopedia for pleasure, and there was a story about a scientist who met him on the train one day and started telling him about his work. It was all terribly abstruse and in the middle of it he couldn't think of a man's name and the reference to his work. Without batting an eyelash, without a moment's hesitation, Popsy supplied it, even to the place, date, volume, and line of his publication!

Chapter 3

DOCTOR-ACTORS

So you see I knew and loved these men and came under their spell. I saw them act, too, for they were all consummate, if unconscious, actors, as are all great men. Every one of them puts on a show, each in his own way. Some few of them know it and do it consciously. It is their way of putting over their message. It is, too, the way some of them play. I think Osler falls into this latter category. He loved to play and wasn't above little pranks. Like the morning he is said to have gone over to Kelly's department and told the women waiting to be examined that they shouldn't be concerned about the old surgeon who would shortly see them, that he really was good, and the tremor of his hands usually disappeared when he got down to operating—Kelly being then all of thirty-two or thirty-three and very serious-minded.

I wish you could have seen Osler come into the Hospital of a morning. It was the grand entrance of a grand showman and it became a ritual. With Old Ben, Negro factotum, bowing and scraping as he opened the doors of the main building on Broadway, and residents, interns, even the superintendent of nurses milling around waiting to take coat, hat, and books, and get the cheery greeting and wave of the hand, it was a sight fit for Hollywood. Falling in step with his resident, he'd immediately start around the great marble statue of Christ standing in the rotunda and make for the long corridor leading to his wards—all others falling in line. A middle-sized man, with swarthy, olive-colored skin, high forehead, drooping black mustache—he'd have made a wonderful-looking pirate, properly costumed—he'd set sail, coattails flying, talking animatedly in easily heard tones, greeting men and women he passed and often taking them by the arm as the cavalcade, pleasantly noisy and laughing at the Osler quips, went happily on its way to the grand rounds. We who were students would be waiting on our respective wards, charts and everything ready, while nurses nervously set things to rights and orderlies flicked imaginary specks

18

of dirt off tables and beds. Even the sickest patient perked up, knowing well that a great event was about to take place.

And great event it was as Osler passed through the doors smartly held open by the resident, greeted the nurses in charge, and immediately proceeded to the first patient—the cavalcade in hushed silence now gathering around the bed. As I recall, he'd never burst right into the examination but would indulge in some sort of extraneous talk while patting the patient on the shoulder or otherwise reassuring him. Then came the history, given in somewhat faltering tones by the fourth-year student who had worked up the case, a few questions and answers by the intern or resident, after which the great physician would make his meticulous examination or just stand or sit there talking. He liked to group things and he had the knack of stating signs and symptoms and causes and effects in such simple language and lucid manner that you couldn't help but understand. Every once in a while he'd listen to heart and lungs with his stethoscope, and his manner of carrying it became another ritual. One earpiece was hooked into his vest armpit, and the instrument hung down from there under his coat. When he was working, though, going from bed to bed, the earpieces were slung around his neck with the rubber tubes and end hanging down in front. It was interesting to see how house officers and students followed suit. Osler really made bedside teaching of medicine come alive.

Everything about him was interesting, especially his manner of handling the sick. With a word or a nod or maybe a question he'd get their confidence, and the things they'd tell him and the cooperation he'd get—even in the painful maneuvers he sometimes needed to make. He could teach and he knew his stuff—whether it was the pathology of the case he was dealing with, the cause, the way it all developed, the way it was going, the history of the illness, the man who first described it. His ward rounds were the pinnacle of perfection and simplicity, and to this day I have never seen their equal. From bed to bed he'd go, from ward to ward, from one illness to another, and never did I see a man or woman leave before Osler completed his rounds.

He used to say the four F's give you typhoid fever: fingers, food, flies, filth. Morphine was G.O.M.—God's own medicine. If you knew syphilis and t.b., you could come pretty near practicing medicine successfully. Syphilis was the great simulator and would fool you. And so on and so on. Great teaching by an inspired teacher who literally oozed personality and had no truck with anything but the truth. They called him "the Chief." They never called anybody else that at the Hopkins—before or afterward.

I wouldn't say that Dr. Halsted was much of a showman—or even a conscious actor. Yet he definitely played a role—a dual, triple role. He played it throughout his entire life, or that part of it we knew, and he never deviated one iota from form. He was two, three, or four personages in one and portrayed each with equal skill. He was the learned, forgetful professor on the surface—always polite, punctilious, shy, genial—but aloof. He'd bow to you if you bowed to him and maybe even say a word of greeting but he wasn't outgoing like the Chief and Popsy. So he became familiarly known as "the Professor," and wherever you went, wherever you were, if the talk turned to Hopkins and the Professor was mentioned, it was always Halsted who was referred to, never anyone else. Men liked him and admired him and were sure he knew his stuff, even if he couldn't or didn't get it across. If he made ward rounds—which was rare—he'd get wrapped up in a single case, congenital hip or something, and he'd examine and measure and compare and talk and philosophize until you'd be bored to death and almost die from fatigue standing there watching and trying to understand.

On the other hand, he'd be terribly interesting and even a bit talkative if you were fortunate enough to be in on some of his experimental work—or were privileged to watch it. For he was a born thinker and research worker. He loved best, I think, the hours he spent in the laboratory, and it was there that he seemed to forget himself and be just a doctor who was engaged on a problem. He accomplished a lot, too, and much of what we know about blood vessel surgery and goiter surgery dates from the Professor's researches. Aneurisms (abnormal dilatations of blood vessels) especially interested him, and he was tireless in his work—and oblivious of time and little things like engagements to operate on certain wealthy or prominent people. They tell a story about how he completely forgot to go to Washington for a scheduled operation and when reminded said pleasantly but firmly that he really hadn't the time, his animals demanded so much of his energies.

But he could operate. I never knew whether he actually liked it—in the way most surgeons do—but he certainly was a different man when he did. He never seemed nervous, he was never in a hurry, neither blood nor unusual difficulties disturbed his equilibrium. You knew that he was the master at all times and under all circumstances, yet there was none of the flash and the fire you'd see in other "big-time" surgeons. Like Kelly, for instance, or the great showman, John Deaver of the University of Pennsylvania—probably the greatest showman of them all and one of the greatest of surgeons.

. Halsted was a philosopher. Halsted was resourceful. Halsted was painstaking—and dreadfully slow. So slow, in fact, that some surgeons who came to watch him left in disgust, while others smiled superciliously and shook their heads. He became a marked man among surgeons, and more than one remarked that he simply couldn't get the man. "Four hours to do a breast. Think of it. Four solid hours for an operation that ought to take but an hour and a half at the most. Whew!"

Poor men. They didn't know. They didn't understand. Not, that is, till long years after—when they had become older and begun to think. For Halsted was a perfectionist, and his operations were works of art. His surgery was poetry—poetry of a sort few men understood. Halsted taught respect for tissues and the control of bleeding. He taught the ultimate good for his patient; and the time element was not a consideration. No patient of his ever left the operating table in shock, nor ever had a bungled, messy operation. When he dealt with cancer he struck for its roots without compromise. When he did a breast it was a finished piece of work, and to this day no surgeon has ever gotten better results, and few have equaled his.

Yet withal Halsted was basically tragedy—stark tragedy. You could see it in his face and demeanor. You could see it in his gloomy, silent brooding. You could see it in his lonely life. They say he had been light and gay, a sort of *bon vivant* as a young man, even something of an athlete at college. He was a man of culture and means. Life beckoned him, and he followed the good trail till fate stepped in and made him a cocaine addict. From that time on he was different, and though he did reach heights of fulfillment, and honors were showered upon him, he was always on guard, always fearful, I suppose, of what could happen! Few men that I have ever had acquaintance with had Halsted's strength of character. So far as is known he never had a relapse.

And then there was Kelly. He was a lovable character—different from Popsy, the Chief, the Professor. More exuberant, quicker of speech and maybe of mind. Nobody ever gave him a nickname. He was always known as Dr. Kelly, sometimes Howard A. I dare say he'd have been the last person in the world to think of himself as an actor or showman. But he was, and a good one. He was somewhat of a mystic—religious to the point of being a bit of a fanatic. I think he changed faiths several times, but he was honest and sincere, and men knew it and respected him. Upon occasion he joined movements for repression of vice and took a prominent part. Too prominent, some men thought.

Howard Kelly was a brilliant surgeon. His fingers actually twinkled. He devised new operations and invented instruments to carry them out. His originality and energy were extraordinary, and he talked well and taught men by the dozens. His assistants, associates, and nurses adored him. He liked the limelight and took pleasure in quick, flashy operating. He'd be in and out of an abdomen almost before you knew it, all the time talking and illustrating what he was doing or about to do. It was glorious to watch him. Incidentally, he was the only surgeon I ever knew personally who indulged in prayer before he began operating. On the occasions I was present he called staff, nurses, and visitors together in an anteroom and read a piece from the Bible or gave a prayer. Brief, sincere gesture that you could see came from the man's innermost being. Commenting on it, one of his long-time associates remarked that he thought

other surgeons might well follow suit. I think many of them do—
but in private and in silence.

Dr. Kelly was a man of great energy and lost no opportunity to
engage in outdoor exercise. The weather had to be awfully bad to
prevent him from riding his bicycle from his home on Eutaw Place
clear across town to the Hopkins—and back again. He was a familiar
sight, pedaling alone through the city streets. He had a private
hospital adjoining his home, and as the years passed, most of his
activities centered there. His work and that of his associates was
predominantly surgery, of course, but much of it had to do with
cancer; that, no doubt, was the impelling reason for his early interest in radium. Certain forms of cancer are particularly amenable
to it, and, one thing leading to another, he became the owner of
more radium than any other doctor in the nation. In addition to
his own work he gave radium therapy to all patients the Hopkins
had—free as well as private. I have no doubt that the Hopkins
didn't want to invest the money required, but it was a nuisance
referring patients over to Kelly's sanatorium and explaining things,
and I often thought it worked no little hardship on them. Dr. Curtis
Burnam, Hopkins graduate of the early days, was Kelly's devoted
associate and right-hand man for long years. Not only did he become a surgeon of great ability himself but he also developed into
one of America's foremost authorities on the therapeutic use of
radium.

Like his colleagues, Dr. Kelly was a voluminous writer and his
clear and concise textbook on gynecology became a classic. He was
one of the first to realize the great value attendant upon good illustrations. It was to further that purpose that he and his associate
and, later on, successor, Dr. Thomas Cullen, brought the artist,
Max Brödel, over from Leipzig and ensconsed him among the residents at Hopkins. I shall have more to say about this in a special
note about Brödel, for it opened up an entirely new field of medical
endeavor. It was not, however, only handmade illustrations that interested Kelly. He thought highly of photography and edited a loose-
leaf Surgery with chief emphasis on photographic illustrations.
Busy, terribly occupied as he was, he spared no pains to get new

and unusual shots, often going out with his photographers personally to supervise their taking.

I shall never forget the time he came out to see a "first" operation I was about to do in the clinic of Dr. Joseph Bloodgood at St. Agnes Hospital, miles away from his own hospital. What a dismal time he had and how patient and understanding he was—how apologetic, too, when finally he and his team had to leave without their pictures. I could have died from chagrin and embarrassment. So could Bloodgood, who should have known better than to extend the invitation.

The case was unusual in that we were going to do a blood vessel suture—so-called reversal of the circulation—in the attempt to prevent gangrene of a young woman's leg. She had Raynaud's disease. Alexis Carrell of Rockefeller Institute fame had conceived the idea and perfected it—on dogs—and I had mastered the technique in the Hunterian Laboratory. This was to be the first trial in Baltimore on a human being. Carrel himself had not been a practicing surgeon and neither he nor I knew or made allowance for the fact that the diseased human blood vessel is much less pliable than the normal vessel of an animal. Bloodgood had had no personal experience at all in such matters and presumably thought it was to be fairly simple—also spectacular. That was why he invited Dr. Kelly to be present.

It was spectacular all right. After exposing the vessels and cutting them in two exactly as had been done on the dogs, I couldn't get the ends of vein and artery together again for the suture (sewing with needle and thread). The vessels hadn't the same elasticity as the dogs', and despite every effort they wouldn't come together. Cameras had all been set with precision immediately above the operative field, technicians hovered about, special lights had been rigged up, and there I was—stuck.* Poor Dr. Kelly. (Poor patient, too.) He stood first on one foot and then on another. From time to

---

* Surgeons will understand that I should have cut the vessels across at different levels, thus allowing for the retraction. That was done in later cases, but you learn only through practical experience. It is impossible to foresee every contingency.

time he'd come and peer intently into the wound, watching the manipulations, now offering a suggestion, now just shaking his head. Bloodgood was acting as first assistant and he literally slaved. Nothing worked. I tried every trick I knew and thought up others, but the ends of those severed blood vessels refused to be approximated, and time was flying. Finally, after an hour and a half of futile struggle, Dr. Kelly reluctantly wrote off the picture taking and left, taking technicians and apparatus with him—but he made a mistake.

It wasn't fifteen minutes later that a happy thought occurred. Instead of tying the blood vessels off and closing up and confessing utter failure—also making things worse and gangrene certain—why not do a transplant?

"How?" asked Dr. Bloodgood when I broached the idea to him.

"Take a piece from a vein in the woman's other leg and splice it between the two cut ends of the vessels in this one."

"Sounds reasonable. Ever done it?"

"On the dog, yes." (I was hell on dogs.)

"O.K.," he said. "Better that than nothing."

Two inches of vein were transplanted between the two cut ends that had refused to come together, and blood flow was reestablished better than before; the thing was beautiful to behold, the operation a huge success—after three hours—and gangrene was averted! Permanently. Thus was surgical history made, and thus did Dr. Kelly miss a wonderful picture.

It takes men of Howard A. Kelly's mold to show the way—and not alone in medicine. How many men of affairs do you suppose would personally go to all that trouble and inconvenience—including the rather painful experience of watching a novice work—just to further an idea? Ninety-nine out of a hundred would have sent an assistant. But not Kelly. He wasn't built that way.

Chapter 4

BALTIMORE. ADMISSION OF WOMEN TO THE HOPKINS

Baltimore was a lovely place back in the 1870's and thereafter. It had a charm and stateliness and culture all its own. The new and the old blended in a manner unusual to most American cities, and even the part that was drab and down at the heels was different. From its situation on the Patapsco River near the head of Chesapeake Bay, its high hills overlooked the spacious harbor, and its narrow, winding, cobblestone-paved streets were obvious relics of dirt roads and turnpikes. Southern to the core, it had mansions of the Colonial type—mostly brick—and they were many and impressive. Yet near by, or sometimes even on the same street, you'd find row upon row of undistinguished three- or four-story brick houses, one built exactly like the other, each with its own white wooden or stone steps leading from front door down to the pavement. Baltimore was called the "City of Homes"—also the "Monumental City," from its many statues of national heroes and battle monuments. An imposing column to George Washington stands in Mount Vernon Place.

From earliest American times Baltimore had been noted for the aristocracy of its citizenry, and as time passed there was a gay social life with romance and no little intrigue. Great personages—also some not so great—came and went both from the Old and the New World, and many and interesting are the stories you read about the goings on of this metropolitan center. So, too, was there big business and great wealth, and Baltimore financiers were among the nation's greatest.

The city's culture, its manners, its fetish for tradition and family and good breeding—also good eating and living—all stemmed from the South from which so many of its citizens came and with which they were associated by ties of marriage as well as business. The Civil War had left no mark superficially, but there were many deep unhealed scars underneath, for there had been some division. Mostly, though, Baltimore was weighed down by the great influx of Southerners who had been ruined financially and had remaining only their names, their aristocracy, their culture, and their fierce loyalty to the Lost Cause. You can't live on these attributes, though, and members of great Southern families found it out to their distress. Nevertheless, they contained themselves with fortitude and refused to bow, and life and society went on, if not as gay and happy and carefree as before, at least with respect and attention to the amenities. Baltimore never compromised in the slightest with its own ideas of its own importance.

It was in the setting thus briefly outlined that the new University was to find its home, and you can see what a congenial atmosphere it was for the men who composed the early faculty. Not that they wished to indulge in high society or partake of a social fling, but that the city was a center of culture and learning and much good living. There was beauty and Southern hospitality and a quiet conservatism—also an intellectual coterie—and however great the aversion had been to Johns Hopkins, founder, there was cordiality for the great men summoned to set in motion the wheels of his project.

Mr. Hopkins had chosen twelve of Baltimore's first citizens to become members of the original Board of Trustees, and although they were towers of strength and attempted in every way to carry out the instructions given them, they could not go through with his idea of placing the University at Clifton, his estate just outside the city. There was his mansion and there was plenty of space—330 acres, in fact—but transportation, housing, and general living conditions for students and faculty made it utterly impossible. The trustees thought it might be feasible at a later date and with that idea in mind they got hold of property on Howard Street very near the heart of the city's business district, put up laboratory and other buildings of an unimposing type, and opened up—temporarily, as they thought.

It is the old story of men making the institution, and never was that better exemplified than at the Hopkins, for a more drab-looking place never greeted a student body. The group comprised some five or six discouraged-looking red brick buildings, four or five stories high, all built right out to the pavement, all separate but within a hundred feet or so of each other, with no campus of any sort and streetcars of the old cable type running alongside. There wasn't even a gymnasium till years later. They were adequate, though, and apparently well equipped, for high deeds were accomplished therein and it was many a year—roughly, thirty-five—until the move to the present beautiful and adequate site at Homewood was made.

Clifton was eventually taken over by the city for a park, but it is doubtful if the Board would have wanted the University there anyhow. With the city expanding due north and west and plenty of lovely acreage available there, what was more natural than that covetous eyes should be cast in those directions? It is interesting, too, that Johns Hopkins the man was slowly but surely slipping into the background, and Baltimore was very definitely becoming conscious and proud of its University. When, therefore, a group of public-spirited citizens led by Mr. William Keyser and Mr. William Wyman made the Board a gift of 179 acres of the finest land just where they wanted it and supplemented it with $1,000,000, it was like manna from heaven. The actual collection of the money and the five tracts of land involved took some three years, beginning in 1899, and if the deal had not been concluded, signed, and sealed when it was—February 22, 1902—the probabilities are that the Hopkins would have been out of luck. The two leaders died in 1903 and 1904, but more than that, the great Baltimore fire occurred in 1904. With almost the entire business district of the city totally destroyed and business crippled for years to come, local philanthropy fell into desuetude for a long time, and the Homewood properties * in all likelihood would have gone aglimmering. It took some years to develop the land and erect suitable buildings, but the move was finally accomplished, and no more beautiful university exists than that of the Johns Hopkins at Homewood with its American Georgian-type architecture.

It never was intended that the Medical Department and the University proper should be together. I think it would have been better

* Buckler, W. H., *Assembling the Homewood Site*, Johns Hopkins Press, 1941.

if they had, but obviously it would never have done to put a hospital out in the middle of nowhere like Clifton. So what did Mr. Hopkins do but buy property farther in town by several miles for that purpose. It was on a direct line from the Clifton estate to the harbor on what is now Broadway, and the land so purchased is the present site (in east Baltimore) of the Medical Department. If Mr. Hopkins couldn't have his Graduate School and his Medical School together, he certainly meant to have them not too far apart—and straight down the Avenue! Alas, his plans went astray, and they are more than miles apart, for the one is in the city's most beautiful residential district, amidst hills and parks and surrounded by boulevards, and the other definitely "across the railroad tracks" amidst dismal surroundings that grow more so with the passing years.

I wouldn't say the location of the Hospital and Medical School affected them, though—in spirit or any other way—and it was a proud and beautiful plant that had finally been erected. The Hospital especially was something to contemplate, having been built on the so-called "pavilion system"—with wards, private and public, spreading out from the sides and rear of the main administration building, which faced on Broadway. The pavilion idea was new in America. John Shaw Billings and others—Gilman, of course—had traveled far and wide, chiefly abroad, studying, observing, holding consultations, getting pointers. Low-lying one- and two-story brick buildings sprawled in a row, sort of like ships lying in their respective slips, each separate from the other, all opening on a covered corridor that ran the length of the place. They laid great stress on air and sunlight even in those days and were especially fearful of disease transmission by air.

Connected by offshoot from the main corridor was the building for surgery, with amphitheater and operating rooms, and adjoining it was the dispensary building, both facing on Monument Street, which ran at right angles to Broadway. The Medical School buildings were in a separate lot diagonally across the street from the pathological laboratory, which at Dr. Welch's insistence was part and parcel of the Hospital and connected with the main corridor. This was a new departure in medical architecture, and there was some hesitancy to agree, but Popsy overruled all objections on the ground that knowledge of pathological structures and disease processes, to say nothing of bacteriology, was essential to good medicine. He has been proved right over and over again.

Housing for the Hospital's resident staff had been provided on the upper floors of the main building, but nothing had been done about housing students or the future faculty. The students found rooms with residents of the neighborhood, but that didn't appeal to staff members. They sought the pleasanter surroundings and better homes across town. With transportation primitive and slow because of the tiresome winding required to get streetcars up and down hills, living across town occasioned no little discomfort and loss of time. Like a lot of other things, though, the traveling had its silver lining because there was time for reading, study—even good talk. Some of the more exuberant men took pleasure in walking back and forth, morning and evening, in good weather and bad. The occasional one rode his bicycle.

So the Hopkins trustees planned and built from scratch a hospital and medical school that was the last word. They didn't have quite enough money to finish the school part and that is how Johns Hopkins came to be coeducational. It is a revealing incident and marks one of the high points in the Hopkins story. A group of socially prominent, high-minded women, who were interested in advanced medical education for women in America, proposed to raise the money needed and turn it over to the trustees on condition that women be admitted to the Johns Hopkins Medical School on the same basis as men. With no other source of money in sight and long delay in opening the medical school facing them, the trustees found it necessary to listen, although with some reluctance. Miss M. Carey Thomas, Miss Mary Elizabeth Garrett, Miss Mary Gwynn, and Miss Elizabeth King were the four ringleaders and they promptly proceeded to form committees in Baltimore, Philadelphia, and elsewhere, with a view to raising some five hundred thousand dollars, the amount that the Board had said was required. The four leaders, incidentally, were daughters of trustees of the Hopkins. Not only that, Miss Thomas was much interested in higher education for women, and Miss Garrett was a very wealthy philanthropist, daughter of Robert W. Garrett, president of the B. & O. Railroad. Altogether, some seven hundred women joined up to put the little affair across and they did collect $500,000 and turn it over to the Board.

It is interesting that Dr. Welch, Dr. Osler, and Dr. Kelly were much in favor of admitting women to the Medical School, but Mr. Gilman wasn't, at least not in the beginning. He was, later on, after certain features connected with the gift were cleared up. It seems that the women laid down certain conditions that the Board and the Medical Faculty found unsatisfactory. It wasn't so much the idea of admitting women as that the independence of the faculty and Board in conducting the Medical School was endangered. The crux of the trouble came, I gather, from the women's insistence upon requirements for admission that the Hopkins authorities thought were too high. This was the time when the masterminds were becoming a little bit fearful lest they wouldn't get any students because they were demanding too much preliminary training—and there were the women demanding more! Dr. Osler is reported to have said to Dr. Welch that it was lucky they got in as professors because they couldn't have made it as students!

It would take me too far afield to go into the long series of conferences and communications required before the matter was cleared up, but it finally was—and entirely to the satisfaction of the Board and the faculty. Nobody but the Board and the Medical School leaders were to have anything to say about admission of students and the general conduct of the Medical School.

It is on record that Miss Garrett gave $354,764.50 of the $500,000 fund, and that probably is the reason she gets chief credit for putting the deal across—that together with the fact that she was the chief negotiator with Mr. Gilman, the faculty, and the Board. But the original prime mover seems to have been Miss Thomas, who had been balked in her efforts to take her Ph.D. at the Hopkins along about 1878. At that time the trustees hadn't made up their minds about admitting women and had refused her enrollment, but permitted her to take courses in Greek under the renowned Professor

Gildersleeve and to attend certain lectures. However, since there was nothing definite, she withdrew, went abroad, took her Ph.D. at Zurich in 1882 and, returning to America, became Dean and later (1894) President of Bryn Mawr College. It was Miss Thomas, presumably, who interested Miss Garrett in the Hopkins project, and no better ally could she have found. I have often wondered why the women didn't demand representation on the Board!

Immediately the Board got hold of the Women's Memorial Fund, so-called, they established the two departments that had been lacking, pharmacology and anatomy; John J. Abel became Professor of the former, and Franklin P. Mall Professor of the latter. This was in 1891, and two years later the school doors were opened. Of the twenty members in the original class there were three women, and from that time on there were a number in every class—ten in my own, 1905. I don't know that they ever set a definite percentage of women to be admitted, but in general there were from five to ten in each class. You must remember that at this time there weren't too many colleges for women in America capable of giving the preliminary training required by the Hopkins, and, in addition, women had not yet taken to the study of medicine as they have in later days. Nevertheless, those who came to the Hopkins in the early days, and in days since, were as well prepared as the men, and so far as my observation goes they have done equally well. Indeed, I think now that one of the best things that ever happened to the Hopkins was the admission of women to the study of medicine. And it hasn't been entirely a question of their scholarship. Theirs has been a softening influence, and no little of the stimulus that we see in students and faculty comes from their presence.

I confess that I have never heard the matter discussed in this latter light, but one cannot escape the psychological effect of the female on the male—regardless of the walk of life. The girl students don't exactly "preen" themselves, but there is no doubt of their being conscious of the boys. How could it be otherwise? It is apparent in their dress, their manners, their actions, in all sorts of ways. There is a camaraderie that is interesting and delightfully wholesome; nobody pulls his punches in talking about sexual matters, the normal or abnormal; nobody thinks of not demonstrating unpleasant things, and taken together the various groups are just medical students.

I never noticed any coarsening or lowering of standards, moral or otherwise, in the girls who studied medicine alongside of men at the Hopkins. They took everything in stride, asked no favors and got none. This is all important, because it is a well-known fact that in the days when the Hopkins first opened, and even in these days to a certain extent, medical students were supposed to be pretty tough guys, and a lot of rough stuff went on during the course of study— especially, if reports be true, in dissecting rooms. One heard many stories of how instructors weren't able to control students and how students misbehaved in many ways—especially at the beginning of their course. So it would seem that it was a happy event when the Hopkins decided to take in women medical students, and those schools that followed suit surely have had equally pleasant results. At the Hopkins we have never followed the custom of stripping or exposing patients unnecessarily, whether men or women, so there has been no occasion for the girls to step aside or to refrain from examining men patients. They have male as well as female patients in the clinical departments and they take their histories and examine them just the same as their boy colleagues do and are responsible accordingly. The women do not take the course in practical male genitourinary diseases—at least they don't work in the dispensary for those affections—but other than that they follow the same course that the men do.

It is only natural that some of the girls marry some of the boys while in school and that from time to time babies come upon the scene, but most of the mothers just drop back a year or so and then resume. This hasn't happened to any great extent but it has happened sufficiently to be worth mentioning. We have a number of women on the staff at the Hopkins and that, too, is a logical development. We have none, however, who are surgeons, and I have never personally known of a Hopkins girl graduate who went into surgery. Incidentally, many of the girl students, also girls in the nursing school, have married staff men. The custom began with the first class, when one of the three girls married the Professor of Anatomy. She did not graduate.

When I was a student we used to do minor operations in the dispensary during the third year—such things as opening boils, sewing up small accidental cuts, and removing little tumors. The girls operated in turn just the same as the men did and they also assisted. I recall one time when one of the girls was assisting one of the boys only to find suddenly that the boy had fainted and was leaning heavily on her shoulder. She merely eased him down to the floor, leaving the instructor to take care of him, and then nonchalantly picked up the knife and went on with the operation. I recall hoping that when I became a surgeon I would have as much self-confidence and *sang-froid* as she did.

I used to think it was a terrible thing to take women into the Hopkins Medical School for the simple reason that so many of them married shortly after graduation and did not go into practice or scientific work. With the classes limited to seventy-five and several hundred applicants for each place, I thought it was an economic waste to accept women and often said so. Now I am not so certain. Some of them do marry, but more of them, I think, stay in medicine one way or another than used to. They seem to go particularly into pediatrics and psychiatry and the scientific branches, and, if reports be true, they do very well. I know several who do general medicine, and they report success. So far as I have been able to observe, though, people out in the world do not care for them as general practitioners. Certainly the men don't, and I have known a number of mothers who felt that they couldn't trust their children to them. This latter was some years back and I think is passing—probably because of the more scientific development of pediatrics generally and of the feeding of infants in particular.

I mention these side lights because they are important in evaluating the place of women in medicine. If I had to guess, I'd say that history will reveal the admission of women to have been one of the greatest of the Hopkins's contributions. It set the example.

Chapter 5

HOPKINS AND THE UNIVERSITY OF MARYLAND. DISPENSARY WORK. EVENINGS AT OSLER'S HOME.

It would be far from the truth to say that the Hopkins first put Baltimore on the medical map. The city had long been a medical center through the University of Maryland, whose Medical Department was the fifth oldest * on the American continent (1807) and whose graduates were among the most prominent of the nation's doctors. It was with pained and ill-concealed surprise, therefore, that Baltimore saw doctors from outside the city exclusively chosen to head the new Hopkins Hospital and Medical School.

The blow was somewhat softened by appointment of certain prominent professors from Maryland and other institutions to a Board of Consulting Physicians—I. E. Atkinson, Samuel C. Chew, William T. Howard, Christopher Johnston, T. S. Latimer, and Louis McLane Tiffany were among them—but it was little more than a gesture. The Hopkins departmental heads rarely if ever called upon the Board, vacancies caused by death were not filled, and it ceased to exist in 1916 when the last member, Dr. Tiffany, died.

The business of bringing in a lot of young, comparatively unknown doctors didn't go down so well, and neither populace nor practitioners had any illusions about the ominous portent of the movement. Least of all the doctors. They could see that Maryland would be overshadowed, if not permanently relegated to a secondary status. More than that, they could see the new and capable physicians and surgeons getting the cream of private practice—if they wanted it—and probably some of the milk, loyalty of patients to the contrary notwithstanding. They weren't blind, either, to the new institution's great resources and they realized that with its high ideals and aims and objectives, to say nothing of inspired leadership, it

---

* The four preceding medical schools were the University of Pennsylvania (1765); Harvard (1782); Dartmouth (1798); the College of Physicians and Surgeons of New York (1798).

35

would definitely be a place of distinction. In short, they and the University of Maryland were sunk.

So there wasn't happy cordiality of populace or practitioners—not, indeed, for long years. The Hopkins did later take in Maryland men and even give certain ones professorial rank, but they were not the "old-liners" whom the people knew. They were younger men, like Whitridge Williams, who became the first Professor of Obstetrics at Hopkins and brought fame to himself and the institution as well. The "old-liners" never did get taken in and naturally they never became reconciled. Moreover, they were right about practice. The Hopkins men did get most of the cream and no little of the milk—skimmed as well as whole. Not the Big Four so much as their immediate associates, assistants, and successors. Welch, of course, was a pathologist and didn't practice. Neither, to all intents and purposes, did Halsted, who wasn't interested. Osler only did consultation work and objected to being pulled away from his teaching, but Kelly cut a swath. He was young and a dynamo and a surgeon of such quality as not to be denied. For the rest, it was the secondary staff and later graduates who did the damage, and there is no point in minimizing the fact that they did plenty.

Nevertheless, Baltimore was a growing community, and there was room for both factions—once they learned to live together. The Hopkins, as a graduate school pointing chiefly to the higher education and development of specially trained men, did not really compete with the University of Maryland and was not in conflict with it. Theirs was chiefly the function of producing well-trained doctors for practice, and that soon became evident. There followed then the gradual infiltration of the Hopkins with exceptional Maryland men and Maryland with much-needed Hopkins men—also the elimination of older men through natural processes—and the atmosphere gradually cleared. Now there is not only cordiality between the two institutions, but cooperation. It should be mentioned, too, that Maryland is rapidly approaching the Hopkins in premedical requirements and standards of scholarship, and I think they would be the first to admit that this has been due to the Hopkins influence as much as anything else.

So the moment the starting gun sounded, the Hopkins went to town. Literally, like a bat out of hell. It had almost everything, and what it didn't have it got. American ingenuity, American drive, American disregard for obstacles of any kind—including such little things as tradition, custom, red tape—triumphed in a totally new direction, and behold! there was a new organism all complete and set and ready to go. Without any of the timid, painfully slow, halting steps hitherto seen in the rise of educational institutions, without the usual childhood, even adolescent years, the nation was presented with a going hospital and medical school for higher education that promised to equal, if not surpass, any the world over. Doctors, students, patients, and nurses flocked to it in haste and with enthusiasm. It was Americana in a big and glorious way.

Thus it would now appear that the early Hopkins fathers did not take as much of a gamble with their new venture as they feared. The very fact of its being unique in American medical annals and experimental in nature contrived to give it needed publicity. The added facts of money sufficient to carry through all plans and the willingness of young, talented scientists and clinicians to throw in their lot with it made its success a foregone conclusion.

The intimate relationship between Medical School and Hospital, coupled with the new pavilion system with all buildings connected by covered corridors, created interest and talk of the kind that stirred the imaginations of people and doctors alike and made them want to come and see for themselves. I can't say what they would have designated as the outstanding feature of the new institution, but they could not have missed its complete "informality." There never was and there isn't now anything of the high-hat between faculty members and students; and the greater the man, the more erudite, the more conspicuous his achievements, the more humble and approachable you find him. There are few exceptions, and in all likelihood it is the system of group instruction that is responsible. The individual is reached in this manner as in no other way, and the student and the instructor talk and chat and exchange opinion and demonstrate intimately, personally, pleasantly, without restraint.

For the first two years the Hopkins medical student is engaged almost exclusively with the exacting work associated with the dissecting room and the laboratories of pharmacology, physiology, chemistry, and pathology. This comprises the foundation of the structure, and if some men find it tedious and exhausting, others do not, and all realize its prime necessity. Many men find time for research, and such extracurricular activities are encouraged. In fact, individual investigation, special work over and above the routine, is a feature of the Hopkins method, and in so far as possible men are left to their own devices and encouraged, as it were, to work out their own salvation. Instruction, didactic teaching, examinations for purpose of review or to show how much or how little is known are held to the minimum. It is all different and confusing to some who, having been accustomed to direction, supervision, and mothering, find it difficult to fend for themselves. They get over it mostly, but those that don't are dropped—or voluntarily withdraw.

Not until his third year does the Hopkins student have any real contact with patients, and then it is chiefly in the dispensary. He doesn't get into the hospital wards till his fourth year, when he acts as a sort of clinical clerk and assistant intern. He is never called anything but "Mister" until the day he graduates, and that, too, is a custom that does not hold for all medical schools. It comes so natural at the Hopkins that no one pays the least attention to it, and you may be assured that nothing like a slight is intended. It is very interesting, really, because you'd think some of the patients would resent being questioned and examined by a white-coated youngster whom nurses, doctors, orderlies, and all address as "Mister" (or "Miss")—but they don't.

The whole class comes together for certain lectures and clinics—sometimes two classes at the same time, like the third and fourth surgical and medical clinics on Fridays and Saturdays—but for practical purposes classes (all limited to seventy-five) are split up into small groups of, roughly, twenty, and rotate from one service to the other each quarter. Thus students come in contact with patients, and staff men come in contact with both. Especially is this so in the great dispensaries, where so much of the best teaching is done. This is not to disparage the teaching done on the wards—the famous bedside teaching of Osler and the others—which is more detailed in that hospitalized patients are observed under treatment, and their signs and symptoms recorded, together with tests, X rays, operations, therapy, and all the other things modern medicine has to offer.

I think first impressions and the early formation of good habits are more important, and that is why I like dispensary teaching so much. There you see illness and disease in the raw. Patients come in right off the street sometimes, often unbelievably ill, and the student sees how experienced men go about discovering what the trouble is—starting from scratch and without benefit of the various and sundry scientific aids. These all come later—after someone, somehow, has gotten a line on things and mapped out a course.

I will say that faculty and students were somewhat closer in the early days—the "good old days"—but that was due to the fact that the place was much smaller and less pretentious than now. Everybody knew everybody else then, and if a man finished up early in his own department, he frequently wandered over into another and helped out—or just gave advice! I recall giving the physicians all sorts of hints about examining chests and hearts, and my feelings weren't hurt one bit when they didn't take them. I didn't take theirs when they barged into my domain, either, but we did have a lot of fun and quite without harm to the patients. It is true that when the Chief or the Professor unexpectedly turned up—as they did in those days—there was a sudden scattering of certain great but still unknown and unrecognized doctors, but that, too, added zest to life.

In those days there was only one big central dispensary waiting room—beautifully smelly!—and, sick to death or not, patients sat on the usual straight-backed, uncushioned, horribly uncomfortable, dark-stained wooden benches facing the door leading to medical, surgical, G.U., skin, or other departments. They all opened off the one waiting room, and the poor souls who were sick had to be there by nine o'clock—or was it eight-thirty—and sit and sit and sit till their turn came. If a woman's baby was so inconsiderate or unfortunate as to be born there in the midst of all the hullabaloo, we took care of that little emergency promptly and efficiently, and if the police dragged in a man who was maybe bleeding from an accident or stab wound, or just some woman who'd been beaten up by her husband, we took care of that, too. Naturally there was the occasional child with fulminating scarlet fever sitting there, head resting in its mother's lap, and perhaps a man or woman coughing and spitting and spewing germs of tuberculosis round about, but nobody bothered much and we didn't, either. We took things in stride; it was all in the day's work, and doctors, students, nurses, and attachés got to know and like each other a lot; and if you think that wasn't supertraining in real medicine and doctoring generally, you're dead wrong.

But time marches on, and the scoundrels tore down that beautiful smelly dispensary to make way for a bigger and better one. The poor souls of patients still do a lot of unconscionable waiting, and the type and hardness and uncomfortableness of the benches hasn't changed; but they sit in several different rooms now, just off the departments to which they are allotted. For though they tore down only the one building they went ahead and added to or put up others, and "the good old days" were done, and I've been crying my eyes out ever since. Doors to clinics don't open on the one big room any more; clinics are widely separated; you can't wander from one to the other as you could before; staffs have grown and changed; the whole place has changed and sort of surged forward. You don't know all the men in your own department any more, let alone those of others—and just think of all that advice we used to give each other and didn't take that's gone down the rathole.

Gone, too, are those very special sessions the lovable and genial Dr. Osler used to have at his home. They were something, and no man who ever attended will ever forget them or cease to be grateful for the unusual opportunity to know and see in his home such a charming character. Each Saturday night, unless otherwise engaged —and he saw to it that that didn't happen often—he had the fourth-year medical group over at his home at eight o'clock for intimate talk and a review of the week's work.

He and Mrs. Osler lived in a lovely old Colonial house—torn down since to make way for an apartment house—across town just off the city's business section, and I can remember yet the awe and trepidation with which we entered the great center hall. To the right was the doctor's office, all lined with bookshelves completely filled, while to the left was the waiting room. One corner of the office room was cut off by projecting bookshelves, and it was behind this that the great physician had his examining couch. The secretary sat outside the little corner and took dictation.

The dining room was back of the waiting room, and it was to this that we were ushered by the Negro butler, who seated us around the big uncovered table. There, over beer and pretzels, with the Chief seated at the head, each man in turn and by name was called on to tell of the cases he was handling, and the doctor asked questions and discussed them pleasantly and informally. Any man could ask questions, and some did. Mostly, though, Dr. Osler did the talking and cited cases and experiences and made comparisons. He had a ready smile, a good laugh, and he loved to tell stories, some of them a bit off-color. In fact, on his rounds he used to do this on purpose and out of sheer deviltry to embarrass the nurses. It was wonderful, and his eyes used to twinkle and he'd chuckle in a sort of personal way that disarmed possible critics before they even got started.

It would be difficult to understand a man like Osler giving up his Saturday evenings to students after a hard week's work if you didn't know the man and his philosophy. He loved people; he was an instinctive doctor; he was a natural as a teacher; he was lucid beyond most men; he knew so much of disease processes and had such deep sympathy for the sick and down-and-out; he, more than any man I ever met—save one—felt the "call." That other man was John M. T. Finney—surgeon.

A box of imported cigars was on that dining-room table each Saturday night, and the butler always brought in one or two big chocolate cakes that looked and tasted as if they were homemade. It was a lovely evening, and, as I recall, no associate or assistant was ever present—or Mrs. Osler. It was just Dr. Osler and us. Each year, though, and as a closing gesture, the doctor and Mrs. Osler used to give a reception to the whole class, and I remember well that the punch had a definite "stick" in it! Osler knew men and life and liked both. He gave more of himself to the students than any other member of the faculty. Others were deeply interested and took great pains. Others had the men to their homes occasionally or did some other entertaining—a reception, a meeting, dinner at a club, perhaps a theater party—but nothing approached the easy hospitality and genuine friendliness of Osler.

Chapter 6

THE RESIDENT SYSTEM

The Four Great Doctors created an aura about the Johns Hopkins. No small part of that aura stemmed from the unique resident system that they also created. It was a break from tradition. It sired a long line of mighty men.

They took on young doctors as interns and followed custom by advancing the best of them to assistant residents, but the one man who finally became chief resident was kept on indefinitely. It was this latter feature that was so unique. Residents of other hospitals, after having spent three years getting to be chief resident, usually left after one more year—the whole term being four years. That remains the custom in most hospitals today, though in certain ones the whole term is only eighteen months all told—and, of course, some, mostly smaller outlying hospitals, don't have any residents at all.

This new resident system at once made the Hopkins Hospital different. It set it apart as an institution wherein a certain few picked doctors of the different branches were to be given training of a special intensive character. Nothing like it had ever been attempted before. The idea was new and intriguing; it couldn't help but attract young doctors of spirit, high ideals, ambition, and intensive drive. It did just that. It also focused attention on the Hopkins.

The underlying thesis was that it was better to train one man well than to train a lot of men in mediocre fashion. It was better to prepare one man so that he could undertake anything in his own domain—practice, teaching, research, even to becoming a professor or head of department in another institution. In other words, the young and eager professors at Hopkins thus served notice to the world that they were out to build men, feeling secure in the knowledge that if they did that well the rest would be easy. It was a bold experiment, but what better setting could there have been for it than in an institution that was in itself a grand experiment?

I think now that this new and different system was the biggest

43

single all-embracing contribution the Hopkins has thus far made, but I didn't always think so. It's like a lot of other things. You don't see them clearly if you are too close; you don't understand them if you are prejudiced or too young or too immature; you don't get the intangibles until or unless you sit down and study and try to think the thing through—as I have been compelled to do in the writing of this book. And lest some think my early antagonism came from my never having been an intern at the Hopkins—much less a resident—I wish to state categorically that that is far from the mark. I thought it was unfair to the many who couldn't be residents and I couldn't grasp the long-term implications—even when they were pointed out. The great need throughout the nation at that time for doctors of superior quality and training who could go out and lead and preach the gospel of better medicine and higher ideals made no appeal to me. All I could see was that a certain few men at Hopkins, who by some good fortune had gotten residencies, became entrenched and ruled the roost with a rod of iron and a superciliousness that grated. For years they held on, and man after man, some of whom I thought were their betters, was compelled to give up the ghost and leave simply because he couldn't stand the gaff any longer, he was dead broke, or his girl wouldn't wait for him longer.

That did happen, you know, and many a man left disillusioned, disgusted, cursing his fate. I knew more than one who held on as assistant year after year hoping for the break, sometimes lured on by a rumor that the resident had received an enticing offer and in all likelihood would accept. Then he didn't, and the poor soul had wasted yet another year or maybe two and was sunk. Occasionally it was stark tragedy, and a good guy was ruined. His luck soured him on the world; his spirit was broken. There was something to be said for my viewpoint.

It wasn't nearly so bad in medicine as it was in surgery, my own field and the one I knew best. I think that influenced me. A dozen men can examine a medically ill patient and they can even try out different things. Only one man can operate on a given case. To become a surgeon you've got to operate. You've got to "do" lots and lots of cases, cases of all kinds and under all sorts of conditions. To be stuck behind a chief resident who persistently hogs it all is depressing; and when you have a professor who places all his faith and confidence in his resident and makes it plain that he will not interfere, it is well-nigh fatal. The accident cases and the night stuff—mostly emergencies and mostly handled by assistants, if capable—do not make up for what you miss of the routine surgery and the aid and comfort and instruction you get from the older staff men. They are always available and ready and glad to help during the daytime but are seldom seen in the dead of night.

What I failed to see was that it all depended on the individual; that some men are made of better stuff than others; some men can take it, some can't; some have it and some don't. Nor was that all. I didn't see that by the very fact of that system being in operation it was possible for men who never reached the residency to develop; that far from the system turning out but the one superman over a period of years, in reality it was turning out large numbers of excellent men, some of whom in after years actually surpassed the supermen. They were the ones who, finding themselves blocked by the man up ahead, remained just long enough to absorb every single thing available—the precepts, teachings, and philosophy of the department's professor, the high ideals, even the atmosphere of excellence engendered by the system—and then left. They were the strong men, the brainy, quiet ones, the self-reliant fellows who got everything but the actual operating, if it was surgery, or actual, complete control of medically ill patients, if it wasn't surgery. They didn't hang around and they didn't cry or curse their fate. They did not come into their own or reach the heights of their development, either, until the long years that it took to get what they lacked had elapsed. They did get it, though, somehow, some way, because they were the kind of men who would; and, of course, they had a superior background of training that made them desirable and welcome elsewhere. They brought with them the aura of the Hopkins, and many American institutions profited thereby.

Like a lot of other Hopkins men, perhaps the majority of them, I always took for granted that the Hopkins was a great institution, but I never went to the trouble of inquiring closely what made it so and how and why it kept on being great. I had a vague notion that it was the superior men associated with it and in my subconscious undoubtedly supposed that their many and varied accomplishments attracted attention. There were hordes of patients, rich and poor alike, and there was a steady stream of doctors coming to admire and to see for themselves. I was warmly satisfied and did not search for basic reasons. Yet there were reasons, one in particular, which I see now.

The resident system created a whole line of "mighty" men. They kept the place running at high pitch and on even keel at all times. They supplied the eternal youth and the eager spirit that goes with youth. Coming from all parts of the country and different levels of society, highly trained, willing to learn and take their time at it, satisfied to make sacrifice, devoted to the masters they had sought out, they walked humbly and achieved riches of the mind. What more natural than that knowledge of the new and different system that built doctors of superlative quality should become widespread and that a continuing line of young graduates in medicine should clamor for appointment?

You could come to the Hopkins if you wished to discuss scientific or practical matters concerned with medicine and find highly qualified men always on hand to help you. You could come to the Hopkins if you were sick and needed attention and get the very best that medicine had to offer at any hour of the day or night, Saturday, Sunday, holidays, wartime, peacetime—whether the great professors that you knew or had heard of were there or not. All because of the superior residents they had trained—men grown mature and experienced yet still living within the hospital walls.

Other hospitals have their lax periods—or may have them—in summertime or at Christmas, because of their key men being away, on vacation, or ill. Other hospitals cannot and do not develop the same type of resident as the Hokpins and for very good reasons. They aren't teaching institutions; they haven't the superior staffs; they haven't the laboratories; they lack the great libraries and medical meetings; in short, they haven't as much to offer as the

Hopkins, and so their young men demand quicker advancement and will not remain if it isn't given them. You have to know these things to understand. There are different types of hospitals, and each has its own problems. Other hospitals, too, have the service system for visiting men. That is, their doctors-in-charge change every three months or so. This is done in order to give opportunity and work to more men. It is a good system and very proper for these hospitals. Interns, assistant residents, residents themselves work under and take orders from these visiting men, some of whom are better than others. When one group takes over from another there may be confusion lasting for days and some laxity. In any case, the residents are not the responsible parties, and that, too, is proper. The house officer with eighteen months' service or even four years' is not qualified to be in absolute charge of a hospital.

It is all different at the Hopkins. They never had the service system and haven't today. They have different departments—medical, gynecological, surgical, pediatrics, etc.—and each has its own chief. He is in charge at all times—whether at the hospital or away, even when ill. He exercises supervision of all activities, and although he may and does delegate this, that, and the other thing to staff men under him, it is the chief resident who runs the show and is at all times in actual physical charge. Whether you like it or don't, whether the Hopkins authorities realized that they had in effect copied the United States Army system, the fact remains that their resident system and its relation to the department chief is almost the exact replica of a Commanding Officer's relation to his First Sergeant. Not his adjutant, who is a sort of assistant. His First Sergeant. And any man who has served his country knows what a "Top Kick" is.

This doesn't mean that no staff man of rank below the director ever comes on the wards of the Hopkins or ever has anything to say. It merely means that he doesn't take over, that services don't change every three or six months. Certain duties may be assigned, and younger men may have a bit more to do during summertime or when the "boss man" is away, but they are very careful not to encroach on the resident's prerogatives, and you should see how polite they are to that gentleman. The outside man sort of "looks after things." That's the way they put it at the Hopkins, and the poor soul who does that is in a sweat mostly, walks as if he were treading on eggs, and more often than not can't wait till the chief gets back and takes the reins himself. Even the chief—say it softly—handles his residents with care. First Sergeants are men to respect.

To become a resident at Hopkins, therefore, was tantamount to being anointed with the oil of greatness. Wise beyond their years, steeped in the lore of the great, accustomed to bear responsibility—investigators, teachers, administrators—it wasn't surprising that medical schools, hospitals, clinics, and institutes sought them out, or that they were choosy and made demands and waited until they were met. I couldn't begin to recite all the positions the Hopkins residents have filled throughout the country, and it would serve no good purpose to do so, but some of the most famous men in American medicine got their start at the Hopkins as residents of one department or another. Simon Flexner, later head of the Rockefeller Institute, was one. Councilman, who afterwards went to Harvard, was another. The list is long, and it has been astonishing to note how many of them worked first with Welch in pathology and from his laboratory drifted or were guided into other channels. Pathology formed their background, and Welch gave them inspiration. I suspect that he gave them other things, too, such as advice and the courage to undertake new and different activities. He may even have discovered aptitudes in men before they themselves recognized them, for he was wise in an uncanny way.

The Hopkins system was not 100 per cent perfect. There are costs to everything, and faults become evident, and both have to be reckoned with. Certain of the mighty men proved to be somewhat less than mighty once they were on their own. Their long stay within the hospital walls warped them in mind and body and unfitted them for life outside. They were so inured to having their own way and being waited on hand and foot that they couldn't get along without it. They were so accustomed to the scientific excellence of the Hopkins—for years the last word in laboratories and accouterments

—that they were at a loss when confronted with the necessity of doing without, or making a compromise, or doing things for themselves. Finally, certain ones became antisocial in the sense that they couldn't bring themselves to the realization that the humblest doctor has a right to his opinion, and so does the patient. In the outside world neither the one nor the other is necessarily awed by the great men from the Johns Hopkins.

These and other things came as a shock to the occasional ex-resident, and with all his learning he found himself at a distinct disadvantage in the world of competition. Little men of limited knowledge and less experience assumed airs and importance by reason of their ways with people and their understanding of the world. More than one Hopkins resident was a flop on the outside. Which is but another way of saying that it's all a question of the man.

Yet withal, the system was a huge continuing success, and over the years the Hopkins has had reason to be grateful. As new and different clinics have been added to the parent institution they have one and all adopted the system, and that is proof conclusive of its high regard. Obviously, there has never been compulsion or even pressure. It was just the natural thing. I've never heard what the average time for the resident's stay was, but it would be interesting to know. They say Dr. Thayer was Osler's resident in medicine for nine years—a long time by anyone's reckoning—but whether that was a record isn't revealed. He remained in Baltimore and later became Professor of Medicine for a time. He had refused a call to Harvard, his own alma mater.

Generally speaking, though, men who were residents have not succeeded to chairs at Hopkins—not, that is, if they remained on as staff men. If they left for duty elsewhere, they were supposed to have a better chance to be called back to the professorship. For this practice the institution has come in for no little adverse criticism from its own men. They maintain that it discourages honest, long-time effort and wholehearted devotion to the institution. I have never heard comment from the directorate, but there have been instances where the staffs of one or another department went on record as favoring one of their own men for professorship, only to be ignored. The staffs didn't like it but were helpless. In the occasional instance it might have been better if their advice had been heeded, but the reverse has also been true. In every instance the staffs gave loyal support once a man, ex-resident or not, was appointed.

In the early days there was room for many younger staff men at Hopkins, and numbers of residents preferred to remain rather than go elsewhere. These positions paid little or nothing, but that didn't matter because their prestige was such that they were able to become consultants or practitioners out in the city and make far more than their needs. Dr. Thayer did this, and so did Futcher, Tom Boggs, and others. McCrae started out that way, too, but later accepted the Professorship of Medicine at Jefferson Medical School in Philadelphia. Certain of the gynecologists and surgeons also remained in Baltimore, and among them were Cullen, Hunner, Bloodgood, and others. Cullen, able, gracious, always a tower of strength, was one of the exceptions who succeeded to a professorship. He was Dr. Kelly's successor from 1919 to 1939, at which time he reached the age of retirement.

Thus gradually the Hopkins built up its staff from its own residents. The earlier men were not graduates of the Hopkins. The Medical School had not been open long enough for that. They were simply doctors from different parts of the country (also Canada), mostly recent graduates who were attracted by the great lights of the institution and the promise it held out. John M. T. Finney was one such, though he did not become a Hopkins resident. He had had his residency at Massachusetts General in Boston and came down to work with Halsted and so cast his fortunes with the Hopkins. There was Cushing, too, who had served as house officer at Massachusetts General, but only for a year or so. He quit after that and came to Baltimore, where Halsted made him assistant resident and, when Bloodgood left, resident. Bloodgood, incidentally, caused Cushing much mental anguish by remaining on longer than expected.

One other man falls naturally into this group, if only because of his dynamic qualities and later accomplishments. He is Hugh Young and he, too, gravitated to Baltimore, being attracted by the opportunities for study provided at the Hopkins. A graduate of the University of Virginia, he served on Halsted's staff for three years but never became his chief resident. Following the death in 1895 of Dr. James Brown, who had been in charge of what genitourinary work there was at Hopkins at that time, Halsted and Dr. Welch—he was always consulted—thought Young might try his luck at it, and that marked the beginning of the great Department of Genitourinary Surgery Hopkins takes such pride in. Young had had little or no experience in this work but he was willing to try, and we know how successful he was.

Indeed, there have been numerous examples of men lower down on the resident or general staff being taken out of the line as Young was and given definite assignments. William Baer was one and he built up a department of orthopedics that was quite in keeping with Hopkins standards. The Hospital School for Crippled Children in Baltimore—separate and distinct from the Hopkins—stands as his real monument, though. And then there was Willis Gatch of Gatch bed fame—once a lowly member of Halsted's staff—who became the first professional anesthetist on the surgical side. Noteworthy, too, is Sam Crowe, who heads the Nose and Throat Department. He was one of Cushing's residents but had never had experience in nose and throat. Yet he built up quite a department, and his work on the ear has received considerable attention. The latter three men were graduates of Hopkins.

So you see the Hopkins developing men and giving them assignments with confidence. I honestly do not recall a single one so deputized who made a failure, and that is an extraordinary record because there was so much to be done. Take, for example, the department of X ray. They had nothing of this in the early days of the Hopkins for the very good reason that the ray had hardly been discovered. Yet in short order Halsted had chosen Harry Baetjer, intern, to see what he could do about it and never did he make a more brilliant appointment. Baetjer became perhaps the outstanding X-ray man in America of his period; his department was all that could be desired; he developed men—only to die a martyr's death from burns.

Another man they took out of the blue and set to doing things he wasn't exactly built for was Whitridge Williams. Graduate of the University of Maryland, he, too, worked in Welch's Pathology Department but he had a leaning for obstetrics, which was then attached to Kelly's Gynecology Department. What more natural, then, than that they should give it to Williams, only a dispensary worker, to develop! The rest is history. Like Baetjer in X ray, he made a signal success.

And then there was Max Brödel, artist. He, too, was a resident and he performed prodigious feats for the Hopkins and, indeed, all medicine. I shall dilate upon him and his activities a bit later on, also on Young, Baetjer, Williams, and others.

When you look at this little matter of the Hopkins's early development with the cold eye of objectivity you must see that in great measure it hinged on the resident staff system and the long line of mighty men thus created. They really paid off.

Chapter 7

CORDIALITY BETWEEN SCIENTIFIC AND CLINICAL
SIDES. ANATOMY AND MALL

THERE WAS always the utmost cordiality between the clinical and
scientific departments at the Hopkins. In fact, that was one of the
nicest things about it. No matter who you were, whether big man
or little man, if you had an idea and wanted to develop it, all you
had to do was seek out the department you wished to work in, state
your problem, and if it was humanly possible, they'd put the whole
works at your disposal. Howell in physiology and Abel in pharmacology were especially cooperative. I knew them best, and others
did, too, because so much of clinical medicine concerns or at least
touches on their branches. It touches on anatomy, too, of course,
but Mall was less outgoing, more inclined to be aloof than the
others, and, besides, most all of the men had a bone to pick with
him. And that's not a joke!

Mall failed the men. He didn't do what he was supposed to do—
what professors of anatomy elsewhere did—teach anatomy. To his
mind downright teaching was not the University idea at all. The
University idea was that a man should work out his own salvation.
Leastways, Mall said it was, and they let him get away with it.
Which was a bit rough on the students, for they never did learn
anatomy.

Mall was trained in Germany almost exclusively, and that's the
answer. It was in Germany that he first met Dr. Welch—before the
Hopkins was opened. As a matter of fact, Welch got much of his
early training in Germany, too. All the early Hopkins men did,
and some of the later ones. Germany was preeminent in medicine
then, in science generally, and doctors from America flocked there.
It was the thing to do then and for long years afterwards—till after
World War I, in fact. You either went to Germany and got it
or you went without. England and France were mere hangers-on and
not to be taken seriously, and America was still primitive.

So from the very start the Hopkins was deeply tinged with German tradition, and nobody objected. On the contrary, the influence was good. But it could be carried too far, and it is my personal opinion that that was where Mall made his great mistake. Welch and Halsted were just as much imbued with the excellencies of Germany; you had only to be with them a half hour to know that; they constantly harked back to the days they spent in the laboratories and clinics of Germany's medical elite and as the years passed they all but commuted between the two countries. Yet they always maintained a sense of balance and did not bear down to the extent that Mall did. They took the best that Germany and other countries had and fitted them into the American scheme of things. Mall couldn't do that—or maybe he wouldn't. Science, science to the utmost, was his theme, as well as the University idea.

Mall was a funny fellow, I thought. The boys used to call him "Johnny Mall" and then sort of make a wry face. He wasn't very popular generally—or even well known. Protégé of Dr. Welch and, like so many others, a worker in his laboratory before becoming the first Professor of Anatomy at the Hopkins, he rarely smiled, had little warmth for the average fellow, was cynical and sarcastic— or so it seemed—and you couldn't get close to him like you could to Howell, Abel, Jones, and the other lovable scientists.

A thin, wiry little man, slightly stooped, quiet and thoughtful-looking, Mall was highly regarded by his colleagues for mental qualities that the students could only guess at. He never lectured, rarely talked to them, but believed thoroughly in the good old American adage of a fellow's getting out the way he got in. Only, if you're a beginner in anatomy and a timid young man, maybe deeply disturbed at the very idea of dissecting a fellow human being, without help and direction you only get in deeper. You rarely get out with any fundamental knowledge and understanding; and if that's heresy, and disloyal to a great man's memory, and unscientific, let those who think differently go and see for themselves.

Mall not only didn't teach anatomy, he wouldn't let any of his staff do it, either. He used to walk through the dissecting rooms upon occasion but rarely said anything. He'd take an instrument here and make a little poke, or point there and maybe ask a question, but he rarely made comment. One or two of his assistants—one was a second-year student named Bean—tried to help a bit, but since there wasn't any definite scheme of things it was hopeless. To make matters worse, Mall didn't like Gray's *Anatomy*, the one anatomy that seemed clearest and most helpful to us, and objected to having it in his dissecting rooms. To this day I don't know the reason for his dislike. To one of my rather practical make-up, the whole business was a mess. When it came to examination I went before him in fear and trembling. There in a big laboratory in a great white coat he gave me a rare friendly greeting.

"Where are you from, Bernheim?" he said.

"Kentucky, sir."

"Going to be a doctor?"

"I hope so, sir." I was so scared I could scarcely talk.

"Know what you want to be?"

"No, sir, except that—"

"See that dog lying over there?"

I hadn't, but there on the table was a dead dog lying flat on its back.

"Open the abdomen and show me the liver."

That seemed easy, and, taking knife and scissors lying near by, in short order I did as directed.

"Now show me the spleen."

That, too, was easy—so easy that I thought there was a catch in it and was more fearful than ever, wondering when and where the real blow would land. For if one thing was true it was that I hadn't the remotest knowledge of finer anatomy. You can imagine, therefore, my relief, my gasp, when the great man said, "Good-by. That's all. Send the next man in."

It has been said that Mall was one of the brainiest men ever connected with the Hopkins, and I guess it is so. It is generally admitted that his research was excellent, and there is no doubt that he trained a group of high-ranking anatomists. Several of his protégés hold chairs in America's great institutions. It is further recorded that he had much influence with Dr. Welch and through him (and others) he wielded great power in the councils at the Hopkins. They say that Mall did not have the gift of influencing men by speech as did Welch and others and never spoke out in open committee meetings. But through reason and private talk he was eloquent, and that, I suppose, accounts for but a few intimates knowing the depths of his mentality.

Even so, I personally think he should never have been Professor of Anatomy—or, at least, had the teaching of it. If you are going to be a doctor—any kind of doctor—you've got to know anatomy, and failure to teach the subject to students is ridiculous. One staff member said to me, in discussing Mall's idea, that he thought it a waste of time to spend long months in the dissecting rooms, anyhow, and to that extent he defended the doctor.

"I think it would be much better," he said, "to have prepared specimens all ready and carefully dissected out for the men to see and pore over. Certainly it would save loads of time."

"What about the feel of the tissues, and the dexterity one gets in dissecting?" I asked.

"Much overrated," he answered.

"It's a unique idea to me," I had to say, "but at least you would see that somehow, some way, your students got a good knowledge of the subject."

"Sure would."

"That's all I'm saying. Mall made no effort in that direction."

Not every student is going to be a scientist—of anatomy or anything else—and first-year medical students certainly do not know how to work out their salvation in anatomy. At least none of those I ever knew did. So it happened that one man's cockeyed idea has affected every Hopkins graduate up to this very day, and if you think that has not caused plenty of criticism you are mistaken. Those of us who became surgeons were especially hard hit because we had to go out and learn anatomy afterwards, and that is a tough assignment, for anatomy can be likened to a baby's walking, good habits, culture. The time to get it is in the beginning when you are young and uninhibited; when, in other words, it comes to you naturally, easily, pleasantly—as if it belongs.

If it surprises you that the alumni made no representations in this matter, I can only say that so far as my observations go, the alumni at Hopkins have had little to say about anything—individually or collectively. Indeed, they have never seemed to want to. They have an official association—meetings every two years in Baltimore—but other than the usual scientific and clinical program with dinner and speeches in the evening, nothing comes of it. Thus in the pages to follow little will be said of the alumni as a body.

But failure to teach anatomy did have its ludicrous side, and well do I recall the bitter complaints—years after Mall had died, his successors followed his ideas—of no less a personage than the late Dr. Dean Lewis, Professor of Surgery at the Hopkins and successor to the great Halsted. Lewis came to Hopkins from the University of Chicago, where years before he had taught anatomy while making his way as a budding young surgeon. He loved anatomy. It fascinated him. He knew it as few doctors that I've ever known knew it—especially that connected with the nerves. Among other things, Lewis had done outstanding work in suture of injured nerves. He was a great operating surgeon and a great didactic teacher of surgery. Several of us at the Hopkins had long known and liked him. We had served in France with him during World War I.

So Lewis came to the Hopkins from Chicago and no sooner had he taken up his duties than he began giving the usual diagnostic clinics to third- and fourth-year students—all based on his usual anatomical theme—all a complete and utter bust in so far as the Hopkins students were concerned. They didn't know what the poor man was talking about. The most they had was a vague idea, and when it came to his asking them questions and quizzing them on the finer anatomical structures and relations—as had been his custom with Chicago students—all he got was confusion, a blank stare, and mostly silence. Talk about embarrassment! Some of us staff men who were in attendance at the new professor's clinics—out of politeness and friendliness—would have sneaked out if it had been possible, but it wasn't. Poor Lewis, he sputtered and grew red in the face; he tried to coax; he was nice as could be; but nothing came, and he gave up. The boys just didn't know.

We tried to tell him afterwards, in fact we did tell him what the trouble was and where it lay, but it made him angry, and he couldn't believe it. So he kept right on in his usual way giving beautiful clinics on an anatomical basis, and the only ones who appreciated them were members of the staff. They were gems, really, and there wasn't one of us on the staff who could begin to match them. You see, all our clinics had a historical-pathological-clinical basis, because that was what we had been drilled in. Osler reveled in history, and so did Welch. Osler had been a pathologist prior to becoming the great physician, and so we got pathology from him as well as from Welch. I have no doubt that both those great scholars—also Dr. Halsted—knew their anatomy but they made little of it compared to the other two subjects. What more natural, then, than that we should follow in their footsteps, and what more natural than that we should be entranced by the newcomer Lewis's different approach?

But it was tough on the students, and they took a terrible beating—for a couple of years. Then, according to the story I got, one of them had a happy thought. Very quietly, without ostentation, he began taking meticulous stenographic notes of every question Lewis asked—with the correct answers. If he didn't get them in class, he got them afterwards. For two years he did this, and rumor has it that he had an ally. Between them they got every question pertaining to anatomy that Lewis could possibly ask—with the correct answers—following which they made up a quiz compendium, had mimeograph copies struck off and sold them for $1 per.

From the day they went on sale Professor Lewis was a beaten man. Every third- and fourth-year student bought them, learned their contents by heart, and the way they began literally "to knock the doctor's eye out"—in some instances almost before he got his question out—was something to behold. There they were, talking glibly of little nerves going to little muscles, big blood vessels branching into little blood vessels, this muscle doing that, that muscle doing this, when in reality they knew little more, actually, than they had known before. Most assuredly they hadn't seen these structures and could hardly have identified them in a specimen.

But they got by. Dr. Lewis beamed. He thought that at last he was teaching the boys anatomy; at last his clinics were bearing fruit—until several weeks later somebody tipped him off!

The joke was on Lewis, of course, and he was too good a sportsman not to know it. There wasn't anything to do anyhow. There are only a certain number of nerves, blood vessels, and other structures in the body, and the field was pretty completely covered. They say that the genius who conceived the idea of a quiz compendium became a multimillionaire. They also say that certain members of the staff purchased copies for their own personal use, but so far as I was personally concerned—well—that is, there was always the off chance of Lewis asking questions of some who weren't members of the student body!

This is the first real opportunity I've ever gotten to air my views on "anatomy as she isn't taught" at Hopkins, and I feel all the better for it. I could have gone to the penitentiary for trying personally to correct the deficiencies in my own education caused by the Mall method, and only long years after the event realized what a close shave I had. It seems that the "diener" in Mall's laboratory did not subscribe to the same lofty ideals as his master and he had no compunctions about selling me an embalmed and carefully wrapped infant. It was the very end of my first year, I felt terrible about not knowing anatomy and I refused to let a little matter of five bucks stand in the way of greater learning. The specimen made an uneventful journey out to our Kentucky farm in my suitcase—right under the eyes of Pullman conductor and porter of the dear old C. & O. Railroad—and I spent one whole summer in the hayloft of my father's barn getting knowledge that was denied me at Mall's great University department. Not till years later did I learn that my actions constituted a penal offense! Talk about becoming a doctor!

Chapter 8

PHYSIOLOGY AND PHARMACOLOGY. DOCTORS ABEL AND HOWELL

It is highly significant, I think, that professors of other scientific departments did not follow the lead of Mall in anatomy. Take physiology and pharmacology. There they at least made an effort to teach their subjects, and if a fellow didn't learn, it was his own fault. Moreover, the men who headed those departments, Abel and Howell, were among the most erudite and lovable individuals it has been my good fortune to meet. Ask any man who ever went to Hopkins—or ever met them if he didn't go to Hopkins—and he'll tell you the same thing. They were as different from Mall as day is from night, yet they, too, were scientists of note and men of great achievements. The men they turned out were every bit the equal of Mall's, and numbers of them became professors in America's great institutes of learning.

As a matter of fact, Drs. Howell and Abel became widely renowned for their researches, the former having been especially interested in the properties of the blood, notably the mechanism of coagulation, the other in various chemical products, notably epinephrine—so important in raising falling blood pressure, combating shock, and otherwise aiding the body's circulatory mechanism. This latter now goes by the trade name Adrenalin and is one of the best known and most widely used of drugs. Drug houses have made fortunes out of it, but Dr. Abel, who pioneered in its production, got nothing but glory. That is, of course, the usual portion of scientists, but I am not one of those who thinks it is right that it should be so. I have never attempted to work out a proper formula for things of this sort, but the growing tendency of institutions of learning to patent discoveries originating in their laboratories looks like a step in the right direction. Financial gains can thus be used for purposes of science, but somewhere along the line the scientists themselves ought to be appropriately rewarded. An annuity might be considered.

60

The story about Dr. Abel and Adrenalin was rather interesting and was all over the Hopkins in the early days. It never became quite clear, and there were several versions, one of which was to the effect that a Japanese assistant stole the work just as it was approaching completion, resigned his position, beat Professor Abel to the punch by getting prior publication, and sold the formula to a drug concern. They gave it the name Adrenalin, and the thief and they made untold fortunes. As I say, this was one of the lurid stories being circulated—with nobody, least of all Dr. Abel himself, confirming or denying it. I thought I'd look it up for the purpose of this work, and sure enough a Japanese was involved but he was not a member of Dr. Abel's staff. He was a visitor to the doctor's laboratory—one J. Takamini, Jap chemist. After seeing and having explained to him in detail the intricacies of his work on epinephrine by no less a personage than Abel himself, what he did was to go out and produce somewhat of a more refined product of the same thing—and patent it under the name of Adrenalin! At the last moment, as it were, an interloper grasped the fruits of ten long years (1895–1905) of painstaking research another man had done. It concerned the first chemical isolation of a hormone, and though not the slightest harm was done Professor Abel's scientific stature, one gets the impression that he was "mentally disturbed for some years." The incident is exceedingly well told—part of it in the eminent scientist's own words—by Carl Voegtlin in a brief memoir of Abel's life and accomplishments.*

Dr. Abel did so many important things before and after the above incident that it's hard to know what to mention and what not to. He it was, for example, who started the *Journal of Experimental Medicine* (1896), perhaps the foremost of America's scientific periodicals. He also chiefly founded the *Journal of Pharmacology and Experimental Therapeutics* (1909) and induced The Williams & Wilkins Company to publish it—at a loss, I feel sure, in the beginning. I mention these things because prior to that American scientists had scant opportunity for exchange of opinion, much less

* Voegtlin, Carl, *Journal of Pharmacology and Experimental Therapeutics*, 67:373–406, 1939.

knowledge of what was going on in their various domains. Incidentally, Abel was the first editor of this latter journal, Dr. Welch, at Abel's insistence, being the first editor of the other one.

Like all the other early Hopkins stalwarts, Abel was educated in Germany. In fact, he spent seven years there working under the world's greatest scientists, and incidentally using up all his own and his wife's savings before coming back to be Professor of Pharmacology at Ann Arbor, Michigan, in 1891. It was from there that he was invited to come to Hopkins by Osler in 1893. He was thirty-six. He said in answer to Osler's letter that he was "strongly attracted by the prospective intellectual contacts with Osler, Martin, Welch and Remsen." Incidentally, Abel was not a great teacher and only upon occasion lectured to the students or personally gave demonstrations. He left these and other related matters to his assistants and saw that they did them while he went on with his researches. It would serve no good purpose to mention them all—either before or after the epinephrine episode—but one that occurred later in life might be recorded here. It concerned insulin, which, as you know, was discovered by Banting of Canada in 1921. Abel with an associate, Geiling, was the first to obtain crystalline insulin (1926), and Voegtlin says this was a great achievement in that "the chemical isolation of insulin has not only furnished a constant standard for bio-assay and a simple procedure for the commercial purification, but what is of far greater importance it has made possible the study of the composition, structure and mode of action of the hormone. Insulin has revolutionized our conception of the chemistry of hormones. . . ."

I feel terribly humble as I write of the Johns Hopkins's great men—more especially the scientists. Try though I would, I never could get scientific medicine through my head, and the last thing in the world I ever wanted or expected was to get involved with men who could grasp it and love it. Yet by a strange quirk of fate it happened, and like everyone else who came in contact with them, I, too, learned to love and admire them. They had a charm and simplicity of outlook that was foreign to anything I had ever encountered, and though most of their talk was Greek to me—and always remained so—I nevertheless liked to sit and listen. I used to feel strangely uplifted and stimulated. Like one sometimes feels after a symphony played by a great orchestra. One doesn't have to know and understand music to be affected by it. They looked on me as some sort of "genus plumber" or artisan that was necessary to them, and at times asked the most bizarre questions about surgery. Lots of what I had to say amused them, and they'd smile tolerantly and shake their heads in doubt.

In Dr. Abel's laboratory they had lunch together, and it was an experience to join them. A loaf or two of bread—rye sometimes— cheese, and milk constituted the chief items, brought in by Charlie Kamphaus, "diener" of the laboratory in name but in fact next to the Professor and the most important man connected with it. With a recently operated dog or two lying around noisily coming out of ether, and smelly concoctions boiling over Bunsen burners, the little group—with an occasional visitor—would foregather each day in the laboratory and, sitting on stools around a rude kitchen table covered with oilcloth, indulge in talk. Shop talk mostly— covering the scientific "waterfront." Dr. Abel led it, of course, but everyone joined in. I often wondered what the visitors thought of it. Some of them came from distant lands, hardly spoke English, and were famed the world over. The simplicity of the occasions, the complete freedom from restraint, the genuine friendship and affection of the participants for each other and interest in their work must have impressed them as it did me.

You really should read Paul D. Lamson's description * of the occasions to get the true flavor. The only reason I make this note is that I was there off and on for several years—before Lamson, in fact—and drank it in. Once, when most of the others had left, Dr. Abel told how he lost one eye and came pretty near losing both. In the course of his work on December 11, 1900, an explosion occurred, and bits of glass flew into his eyes. The doctor's chief interest seemed to have been the skill with which the Hopkins eye surgeons used local anesthesia in their efforts to remove glass from

* Lamson, Paul D., "John Jacob Abel," *Bulletin of the Johns Hopkins Hospital*, 68:119–158, 1941.

the one eye they saved—and his own reaction when it came to cutting through the optic nerve of the one they lost! His associates said that the resultant ocular strain was seriously annoying to him at times, but he never made complaint.

The combination of Abel in pharmacology and Howell in physiology—with their laboratories on different floors of the same building—was particularly fortunate for the Hopkins. Howell, equally the scientist, was more of an executive, teacher, and lecturer than Abel—also more of a writer. In addition to his researches he found time to get out a textbook on physiology that not only became a classic but went through edition after edition.* If you had known the man you wouldn't have been surprised, because he was a most lucid thinker and had a way of putting abstruse things to neophytes that they couldn't help understand. For years he was Dean of the Medical School. I couldn't imagine how or when he got the time and the energy to do so many things, but he never seemed hurried or fussed, and his natural charm of manner smoothed the ruffled feathers of many harassed students.

The quirk of fate that threw me with Drs. Abel and Howell occurred by reason of the fact that I just happened to be around when some operative work on dogs that they couldn't do for themselves was needed in their respective departments, and the job sort of fell into my lap—through Dr. Harvey Cushing. They appealed to him, and since I was working in his laboratory he delegated me to do it. They showed their appreciation in many little ways, one of which concerned allocating dogs for my own experimental work, but more important than that, they gave me their friendship. It was thus that I had several interesting discussions with Dr. Howell on the subject of blood transfusion. That was my chief line of work at the moment, but I knew little about the scientific problems and was concerned only with the practical, while Dr. Howell's interests were just the opposite. Not that he was opposed to the transfer of blood from one person to another. He just couldn't see why they didn't all die—right off.

* Howell, William H., *A Textbook of Physiology*, W. B. Saunders Company, Philadelphia, 1928.

"When you run blood through those little metal tubes," he said, "I should think myriads of minute clots would form and get larger and cause death."

"But I've never yet seen the semblance of a clot that washed off," I replied.

"That means nothing, since in the beginning they would not be apparent to the eye." And with that he launched into a discussion of the various elements of the blood, together with his thrombin and prothrombin that had to do with coagulation, and it was scientifically interesting but admittedly of little practical importance. Even the little bubbles of air that seemed to be getting into the circulation did no harm, and that, too, caused him to wonder.

"It is possible to introduce small amounts of air into the blood stream," he said, "without knocking the heart completely out, but if I were you I wouldn't overdo it."

I didn't. In fact, after that I took extra precautions and filled tubes with salt solution just before the final hookup—and fortunately had no fatalities. One of my friends in another city was less fortunate.

Perhaps I might add that many years later, when I called on Dr. Howell for information on a very different problem—it concerned the stomach, and he was then Director of the School of Hygiene— he reminded me of our earlier discussions on blood transfusion and wanted to know if I had ever had a death during or after one from a blood clot. When I told him that there had been none he just shook his head and smilingly said, "I suppose it's best after all that those who have to do the practical work don't know too much about the science of it."

It was then that I got the idea of spoofing him a little.

"Dr. Howell," I said, "now that we are on the subject of surgeons and scientists, it just occurs to me to ask if you've changed your mind about our little stomach and intestinal operations."

He gave me a look and sort of grinned.

"I dare say you are referring to Finney having operated on me for an ulcer?"

"Well—uh—sort of. That is, you look well and—and—"

"And I admit to getting considerable relief, but I still maintain that you fellows ought to have more trouble with reversed peristalsis than you do."

"Looks like nature takes care of things, doesn't it?"

"And surgeons," he remarked drily.

The work that gained me entrance to Dr. Abel's laboratory did not concern the professor himself but two of his young associates, Carl Voegtlin, later famed director of laboratories at the government's medical center in Bethesda, Maryland, and Leonard Rowntree, later chief of medical service at the Mayo Clinic. They had a project involving the liver that required special surgical work that was beyond their abilities. It was beyond mine, too, but I had a bit of luck and was able to devise something that answered their needs. The professor was only concerned in an advisory capacity, but it was during that period that he got his well-known idea of the artificial kidney for filtration purposes.

We had been having, in Baltimore and elsewhere, a number of suicides from bichloride poisoning, and that, coupled with the old need for something to combat uremic poisoning, was the background for the experiment. At least that is what I gathered when the doctor asked my assistance, and the part I was to play was so simple I wondered why he didn't do it himself. He did, afterwards, or had one of his regular assistants do it, but he never ceased to be grateful, and, of course, I was overjoyed just to be in the same room with him.

Briefly, he had constructed a boilerlike series of narrow, cylindrical, celloidin tubes about ¼ inch in diameter and 10 or 12 inches long (as I recall), and this apparatus, surrounded by salt solution, was to be attached to the end of a dog's carotid artery and that of the jugular vein. He called it an artificial kidney and proposed to pass all the animal's blood through it via the artery for filtration and then via the vein on back into the circulation. To do this he had to introduce a substance into the blood that would keep it from clotting in the tubes, and that was my first acquaintance with the drug called hirudin. This is a substance that the doctor had discovered comes in quantity from the buccal glands of a species of frog (*Bufo agua*) indigenous to the West Indies, from which place he had them specially imported. It worked, and when deleterious substances were introduced into the animal's blood they really could be filtered out through the ingenious apparatus—in part, if not *in toto*. By a process known as osmosis, if you know what that is.

"Bernheim," said the eminent pharmacologist, "if this works and we ever make clinical trial I promise that you shall do the operative work in the first case."

I was in seventh heaven. Boy, what a break! And all for doing a bit of work that was exactly up my alley. Unfortunately, the idea failed to be of practical value, chiefly, I was told, because hirudin was too toxic, and the apparatus was too cumbersome. Time and a different type of apparatus would be required, but to date it still remains chiefly of scientific interest. More to the point so far as I was concerned was the substance hirudin and what might have been.

I was on the lookout for something that would keep the blood from clotting outside the body—if drawn up into a cylinder, for instance—and you can imagine my enthusiasm for Professor Abel's hirudin. He actually gave me some of the precious material for trial in my transfusion work on dogs, and those at the Hopkins who knew what was in the air were much interested. Those early blood-transfusion tubes of mine and others were well and good, but it had become generally recognized that the real blood transfusion would never come into its own until you could actually draw blood out of one person's veins into a flask containing something that would keep it in the fluid state. Once you had this you could keep it till needed and inject it at your leisure. You will understand that the blood—human as well as animal—clots normally in two to four minutes after removal from the veins and arteries of your body. If it wasn't for that characteristic, you'd bleed to death the first time you got a little scratch or cut yourself.

Thus the problem, and Dr. Abel's hirudin looked like the answer to a transfusion artist's prayer. And so it was—or so it would have been if the little element of its own toxicity hadn't thrown it clean out of the picture. In other words, the stuff itself was deadly poison if used in the concentration required to keep the blood fluid, and while you could risk using sublethal doses (borderline, that is) on animals, you couldn't on humans.

So Dr. Abel's artificial kidney had no practical worth—despite much scientific interest then and now—and the same thing was true with regard to hirudin and blood transfusion. It didn't matter so much to the professor, because, after all, his chief interest was in science, but it was a blow to me. I had racked my brain for something that would do the needed trick, and just when it looked as if fate had thrown me something of real merit, pouf! she blew up in my face. It didn't make me feel any better when, a year or so later, a friend of mine, Dr. Richard Lewisohn of New York City, conceived the idea of using sodium citrate for the very purpose I had in mind—keeping the blood outside the body fluid—and made it work. He deserves all the acclaim that has been given him and more. The sodium citrate method of blood transfusion is the basis of all modern transfusion and plasma, but it might have been different!*

In after years I used to drop in on Dr. Abel just as I did on Dr. Howell. There were always problems and if they weren't too busy they seemed to enjoy talking to a clinician. For my part, it was unalloyed joy to sit and listen. It was on one such occasion that I asked Dr. Abel if he wouldn't give a little fifteen-minute talk to a small surgical club of which I was a member that would be meeting in Baltimore the following week. To be honest, that was the reason for this particular visit. The members, twenty-five in all, had asked particularly to see Dr. Abel, and I was the one selected to make the request.

"Now, Bernheim," said the eminent man, "I'm an old man, and you should know better than to make such a request. This laboratory," waving his hand, "is just a little affair they fixed up for me upon my retirement."

"The men don't want to see the laboratory, Doctor; they want to see you."

* Modern science has recently discovered means to render anticoagulants like hirudin, heparin, and dicumarol less toxic.

"No. I can't do it. I'd like to but my days for that are over."

"Aw, Dr. Abel," I started to say.

"Besides which, I haven't the time. Which reminds me. How'd you— Come on over here, I want to show you something." And with that, up he jumped, leaving the sandwich he was munching half eaten, and led me over to some steaming kettles, a set of variegated tubes, and a lot of other gear only a man of his original interests could possibly have gotten together. For one solid hour he demonstrated and argued and lectured, with me as the sole listener, and no clinician ever had a more remarkable experience. Only when it was over (and I was practically exhausted) did he go back to his sandwich and cold coffee, with the remark that I should come again sometime. He had completely forgotten the purpose of my visit, and I hadn't the heart to remind him. My poor surgical friends! How they would have loved to have been with me. But, of course, he hadn't time for them.*

Less well known to the world at large than Welch, Osler, Halsted, and Kelly, Drs. Abel and Howell importantly spread the fame of the Johns Hopkins to the realms of science as related to medicine. It is needless to say that they were showered with honors. Both lived to a ripe old age and continued their researches to the end.

---

* If I weren't too much of a shrinking violet I'd tell you that during the above visit Dr. Abel told me he had always thought highly of my early work in blood transfusion. "But," he added, "I agreed with Howell. None of your patients should have lived." Apparently the two had discussed the matter and arrived at definite conclusions.

Chapter 9

FIVE DISTINCTIVE FEATURES

No sooner were the doors of the Hospital opened in 1889 than the Johns Hopkins Medical Society and the Johns Hopkins Historical Society were formed—and they've been going strong ever since. Not only that, they were the forerunners of similar organizations elsewhere throughout the country. It was the same with the *Johns Hopkins Hospital Bulletin,* famed journal established simultaneously for publication of choice goings on—scientific as well as clinical—at the Hopkins. Osler and Welch chiefly were responsible for all three projects, but Halsted and Kelly, in fact all the high lights and low lights, gave enthusiastic support.

Nothing in the whole category better illustrates the great leaders' appreciation of essential needs than the establishment of these sounding boards. The young and vigorous men summoned to staff the equally young and vigorous Hospital and Medical School required opportunity to exchange opinion, to set forth their own ideas, to talk of their work—outside of routine departmental exercises. Especially was it important for them to know each other, to have contact with heads of other departments than their own, to get their ideas, to absorb their spirit, to know their men—above all, to be cognizant of the work they were doing and the problems confronting them. With the Hospital newly opened and almost overnight attracting patients in quantity, many of them suffering from unusual ills, there was ample clinical material, and scientific laboratories were humming with activities of varied nature. In the vernacular, it was a "natural."

I need hardly tell you what all this meant to the students, and it goes without saying that on the first and third Monday evenings of each month the great hall of the Hospital was filled to overflowing long before the Medical Society's eight-thirty meeting time. It was much the same on that other Monday evening when the Historical Society met, and never were they disappointed in the attendance of the staff—high and low. Indeed, I think it was that unfailing appearance, the very fact of the institution's greatest personages sacrificing so much, in bad weather as well as good, to be present that contributed so heavily to the success of the ventures. Nothing of the perfunctory there, nothing of the pained duty. It was interest, real, unfeigned interest and enthusiasm from the very start, and be it said to the credit of succeeding generations that that is the way it has remained.

Programs were carefully selected with chief emphasis on the scientific, but the clinical was not neglected. Interesting, instructive case reports were made; upon occasion patients from the wards were shown—some in wheel chairs, some wheeled in in their beds, others coming in under their own power. None without their express permission. Examinations were made, X rays were shown, specimens, microscopical as well as gross, were exhibited, visitors were invited to listen to an unusual heart murmur or feel a tumor or question a patient. It was all exciting, and the effect on the youngsters sitting there on the benches was undeniable. Many a man got primed for the higher, better endeavor at those sessions.

Most of the talent was local. There were so many famous men— Abel, Howell, Mall, Cushing, Thayer, Opie, Flexner, Winternitz, Whipple, MacCallum, Bloodgood, Boggs, Williams—I couldn't begin to mention them all—and there was so much fine work going on in their various departments that there never was a dearth of material. On the contrary, there was so much that difficulty was had in holding meetings to the allotted time, which was eight-thirty to ten. Nevertheless, conscious efforts were made to bring in notable outsiders, and that was how from time to time we came to see in the flesh men we had read about and to hear from their own lips something of their high deeds. Some came from our own country, others came from distant lands. If, as sometimes happened, visitors of note were present who were not on the program, they were introduced and invited to join in the discussion with Welch, Osler, and the others, and that, too, was something.

You will understand, of course, that the various component parts of the Hopkins have societies or meetings of their own, some of them sizable and impressively important. They are not entirely limited, either. And so, too, are there other journals at the Hopkins besides the *Bulletin*. Not a few staff men edit or are members of editorial boards of special and national periodicals. I only brought out the Hopkins Medical and Historical Societies and the *Bulletin* as early, highly regarded features of a general nature that gave the institution much of its tone and contributed in no small degree to its atmosphere.

It is the same with the Clinical-Pathological Conference—fourth feature—which is the outgrowth of the old autopsy with physician or surgeon attending if he could get there or was interested. I cannot recall the time when autopsies at the Hopkins were not meticulously done. How could it be otherwise in Dr. Welch's department and with such assistants as MacCallum, Opie, Whipple, Winternitz, Rich? I can remember, though, when clinical men, those who knew about the cases, those who had them in charge, had difficulty making their time fit that of the pathologists. Too often they were present in scant numbers—or were represented by assistants who did not know the salient features and were not, therefore, in position to discuss them in relation to pathological findings.

The busy Osler always came when possible, and what an occasion it was when he did. He had been a pathologist himself; in fact he was pathologist before becoming clinician, and so it was like old home-coming week when he entered the amphitheater followed by his usual entourage, coattails flying, pulling up cuffs and coat sleeves, ready and glad to take over the show, which he usually did. It used to interest me just to watch him, and I never ceased to wonder at the way he'd handle tissues of all kinds with his bare hands. Rubber gloves were just coming into use then, but he didn't wear them. The pathologist did, but not Osler. The pathologist * also wore a gown, but not Osler. The most he'd do was sort of shove up his cuffs and coat sleeves a bit. And then he'd begin talking and examining tissues handed him on a platter by the pathologist— sometimes not on the platter—after which he'd bring it over to the

---

* *Special Note:* Curiously enough I don't recall seeing Dr. Welch himself do many autopsies. He'd leave them mostly to his young men—only coming in for an occasional look or to enter into the discussion.

benches for those nearest to see. They'd then pass the platter from one to the other until every man present had seen for himself and felt and examined minutely—with his bare hands. This would go on for half an hour, an hour, till the autopsy was concluded and Osler had discussed in detail every point—especially those concerned with error or mistake in diagnosis.

You see, it is only through autopsy or at least examination of specimens that the doctor can learn why his patient died, what happened, where he made his mistake—if mistake there was. These and things of similar nature were drummed into us, and one of the features of Osler's weekly clinic each Saturday noon was his demonstration of autopsy material that had been collected throughout the week and preserved for his examination. The abscess or cavity, or both, in the tuberculous lung, the thickened, incompetent heart valves that gave rise to murmurs, the ulcer of the stomach that had bled, the cancer of the stomach, the damaged liver—these and other things interested the great physician, and he grew eloquent explaining and pointing out to students and staff the results of disease processes.

At best, though, attendance at autopsies and cursory demonstration of autopsy material was less than satisfactory, and so it was that there supervened definite set periods at which students, staff, and pathologists were in attendance for purposes of demonstration, elucidation, discussion—the so-called present-day Clinical-Pathological Conference—held in the lecture room of the Pathology Building. House officers or students read histories of cases under scrutiny; staff members, even heads of departments, tell of essential features, interesting developments, the clinical diagnosis, their opinion of the cause of death, together with studies made and therapy used. Following that the pathologist reports all the findings and his interpretation—which in the nature of things does not always agree with the clinician's. Then there is discussion back and forth with pictures of gross material and microscopic findings thrown on the screen, bacteriological studies, and finally the summing up. If I were called upon to single out the one most important feature of the Johns Hopkins Medical School and Hospital, it would be the formal Clinical-Pathological Conference—familiarly known as "C.P.C." Most hospitals have them now.

The fifth and final distinctive feature at the Hopkins is the Social Service Department, and it is of especial interest to me because I was there before it was organized. That is, I know firsthand what it is like to run a big active hospital without social service as well as with it, and the difference is as between day and night.

The Hopkins always had an active outpatient department, and in the nature of things there were many down-and-outs. Sometimes the social element was of greater importance than the physical ill; sometimes the social led to the physical ill; sometimes it was impossible to correct or improve the ill unless the social were taken in hand first—or concomitantly. These and other things plagued us, slowed up the work, impeded it—at times drove us almost to distraction. For we who chiefly manned the dispensary were young and in great measure still untouched and unlearned in the ways of the world. Moreover, we had not grown callous. The older doctors who supervised had taken on that outer shell or crust of objectivity that all doctors must eventually assume if they are going to do field work and live. I take it you know what I mean. To doctor the sick, to note their sufferings, to evaluate the truth and cast aside the sham, to use one's best judgment, to be able to ignore extraneous things like poverty and sadness and ignorance, not to say willfulness, and still carry on, requires an equanimity that can be had only if there is the outer crust of what I call objectivity. Let that be pierced, and your doctor becomes but another human who can be swayed by his emotions and not his mind.

We who were young had not reached this objective stage and so were too often unhappy, discontented—even angry at our helplessness. But we fought the good battle. We fought it with all we had, which was little enough. If it was the drunk who came in and got his busted nose fixed up and then fell asleep on the benches, we put him in a corner and let him sleep it off peacefully and comfortably. If it was the poor soul who came in cold and sopping wet because she hadn't the carfare to ride. we gave her ten or fifteen cents and hoped she'd use it to get a cup of coffee and ride home.

If it was the man who had a badly fractured arm that needed a cast and it was a Saturday, with the dispensary closed next day, we visited him in his home—just to make certain that the cast wasn't too tight and all was well. We didn't have to do these things, we got no penny of pay for our dispensary work; naturally we asked and received no pay for these visits. Sometimes, in gratitude, patients would proffer twenty-five or fifty cents—which of course we did not accept.

I wouldn't have you think this was the general rule or that we were sentimental idiots. By no means. I'm just trying to show you what hospital work was before the era of social service and how some of us couldn't take it all the time. Of course there were the civic agencies, but who was there to call them up and enlist their aid but ourselves? There weren't the usual efficient departmental secretaries then. And besides, the civic agencies were none too efficient or cooperative, though it is fair to say that their funds were decidedly limited and their workers were few. In certain instances we enlisted outside aid and got it, but, of course, that was a temporary expedient. Indeed, I should say that the chief difficulty was never money. You could always get money somehow, some way. Primarily it was a question of people, social service workers, trained personnel, women chiefly—a vast organization that was capable, that had the know-how in matters borderline to medicine.

It took a long time to come and I like to think that we of the early days at the Hopkins had something to do with it. Certainly we did a lot of talking. Certainly we grew eloquent with our importuning. Certainly we tried the patience of the Hospital's front office over and over again trying to get them to admit patients who had no real claim to a bed—none, that is, beyond the fact that they had no place else to go and lay their weary heads. Yes, those were the days. And we who were young learned a lot. It was then that we began to develop our own crust. It was then that we first began to learn the ways of the world. It was then, finally, that the social service at Hopkins and elsewhere came to our rescue and the rescue of countless sick and weary people throughout the world!

The social service at the Hopkins was established in August, 1907, but it was several years before it really amounted to anything.

Chapter 10

OSLER LEAVES. OSLER AND WELCH

In the year 1905 the Hopkins received a staggering blow. Dr. Osler left to become Regius Professor of Medicine at Oxford. The Big Four suffered its first casualty. The Hopkins, Baltimore, American medicine, America itself—all lost the greatest clinician, the most lovable man, the truest friend they had ever had. There was great gloom. As a member of the last fourth-year class Dr. Osler ever taught at the Hopkins, I can personally testify that as time ran out and the end neared, each time he appeared, every clinic he gave, every ward round he made was the occasion of great acclaim and great sadness at one and the same time. Staff, visitors, and students literally drank him in, and it was plain to be seen that he was deeply affected himself.

It seems that the Hopkins had come very near to losing the Chief in 1900, when he was asked to "stand" for the Chair of Medicine at Edinburgh. Only the fact that tradition made it necessary to make application stayed his hand. Osler couldn't bring himself to do that. He came near it in a moment of weakness and pressure but almost immediately changed his mind. It was different with Oxford. He didn't have to make application and it was a Crown appointment. Osler was a loyal British subject and couldn't refuse. Moreover, conditions in Baltimore had changed since 1900. The poor man was literally run ragged by appointments to speak, to write, to hold consultations—especially the latter. From one part of the country to the other he traveled. Big rich and little poor demanded to see him—more especially doctors and their families. He became the doctors' doctor. He was almost the busiest man in the land. So much so that his wife, his friends, and he himself became alarmed lest his strength be taxed too heavily.

That, they say, was the real reason he quit the Hopkins. He was literally driven from America's shores by kindness, confidence, and admiration. To get relief, to obtain relaxation and quiet, to get time to think and pursue his literary bent, he fled to Oxford. The

only unfortunate thing about it was an unintentional misstep he
made just at the end. During the course of a farewell address at
the Hopkins Commemoration Day exercises, February 22, 1905, Dr.
Osler remarked that men over sixty were pretty much useless and
he was inclined to agree with Anthony Trollope that they might
well be chloroformed.

I was present at the address and, like most of the audience, knew
the great man was spoofing. He loved to do that. He loved to play
pranks. He had a delightful sense of humor. But this time he over-
shot the mark. Reporters seized upon the remark, and next day
throughout the land newspapers carried the headlines, OSLER
RECOMMENDS CHLOROFORM AT SIXTY. There followed then discussion, more discussion, editorials, cartoons, comments, mostly carping and critical of the doctor. Letter columns of newspapers were
filled with the thing, and, of course, it became garbled. "To Osler-
ize" became a well-known phrase with a somber meaning. It was
most unfortunate, and though friends and secretaries did their best
to shield him it could not be done, and it is said that the dear, be-
loved man became much saddened. He refused steadfastly to defend
himself even though efforts were made to get him to clarify his
remarks. The whole world took notice, but press comments abroad
were more understanding than those in the United States.

There has been so much discussion of this episode in Dr. Osler's
life that it might be of interest to know exactly what he did say.
Following, therefore, is that part of his address which deals with
the matter. It is taken from the *Journal of the American Medical
Association*, Vol. XLIV, No. 9, Mar. 4, 1905, and I would call
especial attention to the very last sentence. At the time, Osler was
fifty-five.

I have two fixed ideas [he said] well known to my friends, harmless
obsessions with which I sometimes bore them, but which have a direct
bearing on this important problem. The first is the comparative uselessness of men above forty years of age. This may seem shocking, and yet
read aright the world's history bears out the statement. Take the sum of
human achievement in action, in science, in art, in literature—subtract
the work of the men above forty, and while we should miss great treas-

ures, even priceless treasures, we would practically be where we are today. It is difficult to name a great and far-reaching conquest of the mind which has not been given to the world by a man on whose back the sun was still shining. The effective, moving, vitalizing work of the world is done between the ages of twenty-five and forty years—these fifteen golden years of plenty, the anabolic or constructive period, in which there is always a balance in the mental bank and the credit is still good. In the science and art of medicine, there has not been an advance of the first rank which has not been instituted by young or comparatively young men. Vesalius, Harvey, Hunter, Bichat, Laennec, Virchow, Lister, Koch—the green years were yet on their heads when their epoch-making studies were made. To modify an old saying, a man is sane morally at thirty, rich mentally at forty, wise spiritually at fifty—or never. . . .

My second fixed idea is the uselessness of men above sixty years of age, and the incalculable benefit it would be in commercial, political, and in professional life if, as a matter of course, men stopped work at this age. Donne tells us in his "Biathanatos" that by the laws of certain wise states sexagenarii were precipitated from a bridge, and in Rome men of that age were not admitted to the suffrage and they were called *Depontani* because the way to the senate was *per pontem*, and they from age were not permitted to come hither. In that charming novel, "The Fixed Period," Anthony Trollope discusses the practical advantages in modern life of a return to this ancient usage, and the plot hinges on the admirable scheme of a college into which at sixty men retired for a year of contemplation before a peaceful departure by chloroform. That incalculable benefits might follow such a scheme is apparent to anyone who, like myself, is nearing the limit, and who has made a careful study of the calamities which may befall men during the seventh and eighth decades! Still more when he contemplates the many evils which they perpetuate unconsciously, and with impunity! As it can be maintained that all the great advances have come from men under forty, so the history of the world shows that a very large proportion of the evils may be traced to the sexagenarians—nearly all the great mistakes politically and socially, all of the worst poems, most of the bad pictures, a majority of the bad novels, not a few of the bad sermons and speeches. It is not to be denied that occasionally there is a sexagenarian whose mind, as Cicero remarks, stands out of reach of the body's decay. Such a one has learned the secret of Hermippus, that ancient Roman who, feeling that the silver cord was loosening, cut himself clear from all companions of his own age and betook himself to the company of young men, mingling with their games and studies, and so lived to the age of 153, *puerorum halitu refocillatus et educatus.* And there is truth in the story, since it is only those who live with the young who maintain a fresh outlook on the new problems of the world.

The teacher's life should have three periods—study until twenty-five, investigation until forty, profession until sixty, at which age I would have him retired on a double allowance. Whether Anthony Trollope's suggestion of a college and chloroform should be carried out or not, I have become a little dubious, as my own time is getting so short.

Osler was too human a man and too exuberant to allow the episode permanently to affect his life—even though the matter never did die completely away. He visited the Hopkins twice after leaving, and it was my good fortune to see him both times. He was the same buoyant man and took delight in revisiting the scene of his former activities. He made ward rounds, gave clinics, and was royally entertained, even feted, wherever he went. As is well known, he was Sir William when he returned. Incidentally, he had had the same success in England as in America and had endeared himself to people and profession alike—even to becoming practically the most prominent doctor over there. His home was the mecca for American doctors till the day of his death and this, too, was tragic in that it followed soon after the death in action (World War I) of his and Mrs. Osler's only son, Revere. He made no complaint but faded rapidly and died on December 29, 1919.

Needless to say, the Hopkins was never quite the same without Osler. At the close of the exercises on that fateful Commemoration Day, Dr. Welch presented him as "the chief ornament of our medical faculty" to President Remsen for honorary LL.D., the only one conferred that year, and I was on the point of saying that about sums it up—but it doesn't. Osler was far more than an ornament. He was the living embodiment of vibrant life. He was the soul of the Hopkins and will remain so till the end of time, just as Welch was the mastermind and will remain so till the end of time.

They appointed Dr. Lewellys F. Barker—Canadian and graduate of Toronto—to succeed Osler, and opinion was divided as to the wisdom displayed. It was a flyer of the Wall Street type, and I dare say the Hopkins masterminds knew it. Barker wasn't a physician at all. True, he had been assistant resident physician on Osler's staff earlier but only for a short time, having switched over to pathology. From that he went to anatomy, then back to pathology, all at the Hopkins, finally ending up in 1900 as Professor of Anatomy at the University of Chicago. It was from this position that they called him back to the Hopkins to take over the brilliant Osler's post, and if ever a man was put on the spot it was Barker.

Nothing daunted, he took over, but not without hours and days, weeks and months of boning up in the hospital's library. I used to see him there myself and wondered, as did lots of others. A tall, slender, pleasant-spoken, ascetic-looking man, with iron gray hair, handsome face, and chiseled features, he'd smile and nod to us and go back to his studying. I should say, though, that his staff served him well, more particularly the highly capable Dr. Rufus Cole,* his resident physician and virtual shadow on ward rounds and at clinics.

So Barker carried on in the Osler tradition of bedside teaching, but he did more. He introduced or added to the medical clinic great laboratories of physiology, bacteriology, and chemistry—adequately staffed with research men and adequately equipped. It was the first time in America that a major medical clinic of a major hospital had pointed in that manner to the new and different medicine and it not only created favorable comment but caused other, indeed practically all first-grade medical institutions to follow suit.†

Barker himself was not a great research man and did not pose as one. He was essentially an organizer but, believe it or not, he became, in addition, a great teacher and clinician. In fact, Barker became a figure of considerable stature in American medicine, and quite on his own. It wasn't surprising, therefore, that he was much

* Later Physician-in-chief and Director of the Hospital at Rockefeller Institute and investigator of renown.

† Chesney, Alan M., *The Johns Hopkins Hospital and the Johns Hopkins School of Medicine: A Chronicle. Vol. I. Early Years. 1867–1893*, Johns Hopkins Press, Baltimore, 1943.

sought after for clinical and other engagements. Though not possessed of Osler's personality, he had a nice manner; students, doctors, and patients liked him, and he built up a large and lucrative private consultation practice. His critics said it was too lucrative and not in the Hopkins tradition!

It is thus obvious that the departure of Osler did no permanent damage to the Hopkins. Nothing comparable to that which must have followed had Dr. Welch left or died at that early period. That would have been unmitigated disaster—both to the Hopkins and to American medicine as well. For Welch was primarily the statesman and he had grandiose ideas, many of which had not yet been broached, much less carried out. Welch's work at the Hopkins was never finished really, but Osler's was—his chief work, that is—and it is more than possible he was aware of it. He might well have felt that others could be found who would carry forward the work he had started. That never would have been so if Welch had been lost, and I do not feel that this viewpoint in any way lowers one's estimation of Osler or affects his stature. This despite the fact that he had had great share in setting the pace at the Hopkins, giving the inspiration, creating the aura.

Osler's interest, broad though it was, did not encompass the cosmos of medicine in the sense of his embarking on new and different ventures. It would hardly have been in the Oslerian manner, for example, to project a School of Hygiene and Public Health and then resign his Professorship of Medicine to become head of the new school for purposes of organizing and early direction. I could see him becoming Professor of the History of Medicine, perhaps, but not the other. Osler was primarily the physician, and medicine, patients, doctors, students, and teaching were his concern chiefly— together with writing.

While I think the eminent doctor's departure was not a mortal blow to the Hopkins in the purely professional sense, I am not so certain that it wasn't far more serious in a different direction than was generally recognized. I refer to Osler's way with people, his ability to influence them—without seeming to try—his constant willingness, even joy, in doing things for others, more especially the sick and down-and-out, more especially the Hopkins. He had ability apparently equal to that of Dr. Welch to open rich men's purses—and that was no mean ability. Rich people, philanthropists, and people of less means sought his favor and loved nothing better than to further his projects, of which he had many.

When, for instance, the big fire of 1904 wiped out most of Baltimore's business district and seriously compromised the Hopkins Hospital by loss of revenue from destroyed holdings of the Johns Hopkins estate, Osler became worried and promptly sent word to John D. Rockefeller. Others did, too, of course, but more than likely it was Osler's influence chiefly that promptly brought the great philanthropist's financial agent down for investigation—and aid, to the extent of $500,000! John D. Rockefeller, Jr., sent a personal note to Osler saying that his father had taken care of the little affair.

And then there was the time Henry Phipps sent him a little matter of $10,000 which he hoped he'd use wisely. A special dispensary for tuberculosis was in Osler's mind, and strangely enough, Mr. Phipps got wind of it. They named the dispensary after that gentleman—the same gentleman, by the way, who gave the Psychiatric Clinic that bears his name.

There were other projects—many of them—and some concerned men who needed financing. He gave of his own funds, too, though he was not a rich man. When he went to Boston to lecture on "Science and Immortality" he gave the honorarium to the Boston library to purchase cases for special books. But few knew of these little things.

These and their like were what you might expect of a great man, a broad humanitarian. Yet Osler had still another side. He was intensely devoted to his own men. This, too, you might have expected, but not, I think, in the close personal way in which it was revealed. As his young residents—and an occasional man like Cushing, who had not served under him—completed their hospital terms and went out into practice, Osler practically took them to live with him in his own home. They became his famous so-called "latch-keyers" from the fact that they set up bachelor quarters in the

house next door to his and were in and out of his house all the time
with their own personal front-door keys. Besides being a prodigious
writer Osler was an avid book collector and had a wonderful library.
His young protégés—McCrae, Futcher, Jacobs, Cushing—were
kindred souls in their love for literature and not only aided him
in his writing but spent hours and hours browsing in his library,
talking, studying, having tea with Mrs. Osler and generally being
members of the family.

If you were to read John F. Fulton's recent biography of Cushing, you'd find the most charming account of these latchkeyers
written by Cushing himself. The group knew well what close association with a man of Osler's superior attainments was bound to
mean to them in after years, and they were not mistaken. Osler
regarded them almost in the light of cherished sons and lavished
affection on them as only a father could. He was fond of other men,
too, and over and over again was at pains to give them instruction
and advice and counsel, but his little band of bachelor latchkeyers
was closest to his heart. Even after they married and left the abode
next door, as one by one they did, no change of relationship was
noted. On the contrary, the great master merely extended it to include their wives and later on their children.

When Osler finally left the Hopkins for Oxford these men went
along to be present at his inauguration, and that in itself was a
touching tribute of affection. They made merry with the Chief all
the way across the ocean—that story, too, is told—and Dr. Osler
was one of those who read mock medical papers at the mock
medical society he himself organized with the ship's doctor and
other medical men aboard. They had lots of fun but their desperate
sorrow at parting can be read between the lines.

Yes, Osler was quite a man in quite a lot of different ways. He
was too smart not to know that he had what it takes in a big way.
His demeanor, his conduct—he loved a show and it was always a
good one—his manner of life, his love of epigrams, his easy, confi-
dent approach, everything proves that. But there was never anything
cheap about him, nothing of the grandstand. Acting was his natural
métier; his whole life was theatrical, and he enjoyed it to the full.

You only had to look at his face and hear him laugh, see the twinkle in his eye, watch his gestures, to know that. Yet withal I would doubt if he ever realized what a real wonder he was or how much of an asset he was to the Hopkins—and the world—in ways other than medicine.

I would doubt, too, whether he selected Barker or anybody else as his successor. Deeply attached as he was to his assistants and associates, unwilling to cause pain by choosing one in preference to the other, it would be my feeling that he gave no advice whatsoever. If I had to hazard a guess, I'd say that a Committee selected Dr. Barker—there's always a Committee—but that somewhere in the background there was a little, rotund man who was affectionately known as Popsy. I would add that hovering still further in the background was one Franklin P. Mall. A little, thin, wiry man, very intellectual, preferring gumshoe tactics, he frequently whispered into Popsy's ear and thus had more influence at the Hopkins than was generally suspected. He and Barker had been very close. Mall was Professor of Anatomy at the Hopkins, and Barker had been a member of his staff—Welch's, too. It is strange how things in this world work out.

Chapter 11

HARVEY CUSHING AND THE HUNTERIAN LABORATORY

Among the many men who came to the Hopkins, achieved greatness, and shed glamour and renown on the institution, Harvey Cushing must take high rank. The world was his horizon, and properly so, because he was a many-sided man with an intellect of surprising quality. Greatness was literally written all over him—from the beginning. Moreover, he knew it. No man would have kept through life all the correspondence he received from practically all sources, and all the various papers and things generally, filed and indexed, unless he expected them to be used, which is but another way of saying that he expected to do big things! He wasn't mistaken, and though you might say it took something of an egotist to keep such records the fact remains that he was justified. One has only to read John F. Fulton's monumental biography of him * to be convinced of that.

The men who came to the Hopkins at the beginning were near supermen. That is an extravagant statement and not the first one I have made in this discourse, but all you've got to do to be convinced is to "look at the record." Consider this man Cushing—thin, medium-sized, muscular, chiseled features, snapping eyes, quick-thinking, quick-acting, short-tempered, nervous, charming, sarcastic, inconsiderate, impatient, ruthless (depending on changing moods), jealous, lovable, selfish, domineering, demanding—he had a penetrating mind, stupendous ability, and there was nothing he couldn't do and do well once he decided to have a go at it.

The Hopkins did not seek him, he sought the Hopkins. And that's what I mean when I say those early stalwarts were touched, as it were, by the wand of destiny. Cushing applied to Halsted for a residency in surgery but he wasn't so certain that it was wise. He had graduated at Harvard and was a house officer at Massachusetts

---

* Fulton, John F., *Harvey Cushing: A Biography*, Charles C. Thomas, Publisher, Springfield, Ill., 1946.

General, one of the oldest and most famous of American hospitals, and he wasn't sure that he hadn't better stay there. But when Dr. Halsted didn't answer his request as promptly or definitely as Cushing thought he should, he characteristically didn't like it; and it took no little persuasion on the part of his doctor-father and doctor-brother, both seeing the Hopkins with perhaps more mature eyes than he did, to convince him that in Baltimore lay his great opportunity. He did become Halsted's resident, but not immediately. He became assistant resident first (1896), playing second fiddle to Joseph C. Bloodgood, also one of the Hopkins stalwarts, and chief resident at the time. But even there fate played into his hands, because Bloodgood was engaged in the hernia work Dr. Halsted had assigned to him and was compelled to leave much of the operating and managing of the clinic to Cushing, who was then twenty-seven years old and unmarried. In 1897 he became resident in actuality and held the post four years. Incidentally, at that time Dr. Osler was forty-seven and Halsted forty-five.

It is interesting that Cushing didn't like the work or the Hopkins at first and again had to be bolstered by his father. He wasn't particularly enamored of Baltimore, either, but that has been true of many "foreigners" who immigrated to the Hopkins and found Baltimore, its inhabitants, and its unique customs hard to take at first. Later on you get to know people better, and the old place grows on you, and what with one thing and another—the oysters, the crabs, the terrapin, the Southern hospitality once you get through the outer shell, the genial friendliness—you find yourself a Baltimorean. Cushing was no exception.

Fulton's biography is a book of 754 pages, so you will understand why it is impossible to tell the story of Cushing in detail here. All I can do is give some of the high lights, together with certain personal notes of an illuminating character. I worked under Cushing—in his laboratory—for five years, and they were the best years of my professional life.

It isn't generally known that Cushing first brought the X ray to the Hopkins. He had been interested in it at Massachusetts General and brought the makings of a rude but workable apparatus with him when he came to Baltimore. He did some work in it throughout his residency, but his first love was surgery, and he turned X ray over to others. He was meticulous in working up his cases, a perfectionist in his operating, and that, coupled with his mental attributes, promptly endeared him to Halsted. It wasn't long, either, before Dr. Osler and Dr. Welch recognized his sterling qualities, and there arose a mutual friendship and respect that persisted throughout life. Undoubtedly Cushing gained much by these associations, but it cannot be said to have been entirely one-sided.

It would seem that neurology interested Cushing even as a student, but he didn't really get down to it until after his residency at Hopkins and a year's trip abroad in 1900–1901. Then he went into private practice in Baltimore and did what came to him—which wasn't too much—and once was urged to take up orthopedics. There was, however, the occasional brain case at the Hopkins, to say nothing of other things of a neurological nature, and at Dr. Halsted's suggestion Cushing became interested and, one thing leading to another, gradually found himself growing enthusiastic. He had no competition. Not only that, his early mortality rate was so high that at one time the question of his giving up the work arose. I myself recall the remark Dr. Halsted was said to have made, to wit, he "didn't know whether to say poor Cushing's patients or Cushing's poor patients."

But he persevered, and the modern place of brain surgery and neurosurgery is due in great measure to him. Among his initial exploits was relief of facial neuralgia by attack on the Gasserian ganglion. Very early, too, he became interested in gigantism and acromegaly, due to dysfunction of the pituitary gland—tumor, cyst —and he was really on his way. He had operative difficulties of almost insurmountable character but possessed the courage and ingenuity to overcome most of them. He devised new and different approaches to brain tumors, and better saws and burrs. He also devised an electric affair for better localization of centers in the exposed brain. Little wonder that he became "testy" and tough with assistants and nurses—even to the point of being cautioned by Dr. Osler.

His field was virgin, and with tangible results appearing—made known through publication and addresses—once again the Hopkins was treated to a visitation of patients and doctors, and still another avenue of widespread interest was created. It would take me too far afield to tell you all the different kinds of work the great man did in his chosen field or the innumerable cases that came to him— the great army man, General Leonard Wood, was a successful case— but the record is inspiring, and a whole school of neurosurgeons grew up. Starting from scratch, it took study, observation, especially animal experimentation, and that is how the Hopkins came to have a special laboratory for that purpose before most other institutions.

They had been giving a course of a sort in animal surgery to third-year students almost from the time the Medical School opened, and it had been in charge of Dr. J. M. T. Finney, but quarters were cramped, and Dr. Finney was too busy to give it real attention. So it was turned over to Cushing when he came back from Europe following his residency, and he promptly decided that quarters in the Anatomy Building would not do. What he wanted was a separate building and, not being bashful, he said so—and got it, but not till two years or so later, in 1904. It was little more than a small shell of a low-lying brick structure, basement and one story,* set between the big Anatomy and Physiology Buildings—cost, $15,000! They named it the Hunterian Laboratory for Experimental Medicine and Surgery, and that little affair was the real forerunner of practically all the special laboratories for experimental surgery in America today. Incidentally, Cushing and the Surgical Department got only half of it; the other half went to the Department of Pathology.

I should imagine that in the last analysis Cushing will be chiefly remembered at the Hopkins for establishing the Hunterian (1904), and incidentally there is a good story about the naming of it. Cushing wished to call it the Magendie Laboratory but was dissuaded because Magendie's name was anathema to the antivivisec-

* More recently considerably enlarged.

tionists. Dr. Welch suggested that it be named after John Hunter, the great British experimentalist, and that proved to be a happy solution. Lots of people who didn't quite understand thought it had reference to pointers and setters—also horses engaged in hunting—and gave support whereas they might not otherwise have done so. The veterinary tinge created confidence! *

It was in the Hunterian that Cushing really began to teach operative surgery; it was there that he did practically all his own experimental work, and that Dr. Halsted and all other Hopkins men of the time did theirs. For Cushing not only welcomed others to come and work, he was untiring in helping them. That is how I came to know and admire him—even if at times he was tough. A man did not have to work on his own problem or idea. All he had to do was convince the "Master" that he meant business, and he'd supply the problem. Later on, if he got ideas of his own, and the doctor was convinced that they were worth while, he was privileged to work them out—on his own. As he grew more experienced it was not necessary to go to the doctor at all for permission. It was necessary, though, for those who could possibly afford it to pay for new and special instruments or devices required and a laboratory helper, since the laboratory's budget was extremely limited. Dr. Cushing kicked back his salary of $500 a year in order to pay his laboratory doctor in charge, each year a new and recent graduate, at least a pittance for living!

But Cushing was no angel to work with and he could be plainspoken and abrupt. There was the article he told me to write at the end of my first year's work and bring to him. The problem concerned some new and very difficult surgery of the heart, and he had suggested it. He took one look at the four or five pages I brought him, tore them up, threw them into the wastepaper basket and said, "Write 'em over." No more, no less. He did the same thing next time, but on the third effort only marked through them all with a red pencil. I was improving. On the fourth effort he just

* I have given the reference to Fulton's biography of Cushing but wish further to acknowledge the great debt I owe to this superlative work.

groaned. "Bernheïm," he said, "you don't even know how to write English, do you?"

"No, sir. I guess not."

"Tell you what you do. Go home and try once again and day after tomorrow come over to my house [we were in the laboratory] at two o'clock."

At the appointed hour there I was—with my fifth effort—and for two and a half solid hours we sweated out that little insignificant article, and I never saw such an exhibition in my life. He'd write a paragraph and then rewrite it. He'd transpose this and transpose that. This word would be wrong; that one hadn't the shade it should have. He'd go to the dictionary time and time again. He'd consult medical books, even the encyclopedia. When it * was finally finished I was a complete and utter wreck, but Cushing was smiling and alert as ever!

And that wasn't all. He took the same pains with me and, of course, with the others, each time I wrote anything coming from his laboratory, until he was convinced that I could write properly. Not only that, when I was invited to give a little résumé of some work before the local medical society and dutifully brought the little piece to him for review, he said, "This is all right, but you mustn't read it. Talk it."

"But—but—" I began to stammer.

"Make several headings," he went on, "and put them on little cards the size of visiting cards and talk from them. You shouldn't have more than four or five of them and only a few words in big, easily read letters on each; just enough to refresh your memory."

"Golly!" I said. "I'm scared to death. It's my very first time, and suppose some doctor questions me?"

He smiled. "This is your own original work and presumably you know more about it than anybody else. It shouldn't be difficult for you to debate it, if need be."

It wasn't.

* Bernheim, Bertram M., "Experimental Surgery of the Mitral Valve," *Bulletin of the Johns Hopkins Hospital*, vol. XX, no. 217, April, 1909.

From the day the Hunterian Laboratory for Experimental Medicine and Surgery opened (1904), the S.P.C.A. began camping on its trail. Frequently they slowed up the work—occasionally they stopped it completely—but it was never longer than a week, and efforts to close the laboratory permanently failed dismally. This despite determined efforts on the part of openly antagonistic members and a lot of gullible nonmembers.

The trouble is that in these United States of ours everyone has a pet animal, and anything that remotely threatens their Rover or Gertrude, or little Johnny's mongrel Pudgy, or Aunt Maria's lazy, good-for-nothing cat that's always occupying the only comfortable chair in the room, rings the bell of danger, and they are easy prey for the misguided and the demagogue. If it wasn't for that, I don't believe the S.P.C.A. would get to first base with its battle against animal experimentation. You can't reason with people who have been sold a bill of goods about how doctors steal dogs and take 'em to their dirty, smelly laboratories and torture them to death out of sheer meanness. You can't argue with people who have been convinced by that nice Mrs. Elvira Kenworth of "The Kenworths" out in Quevelva Valley that the doctors never learned a single thing from torturing animals that they could not have learned easier and better by other means. You get a hookup between ignorance and the emotions, and the combination is well-nigh unbeatable. Especially if you're not overly smart yourself.

I never thought the doctors were smart. They never took the trouble to learn how to capitalize on their own powers, and such things as engaging publicity experts never entered their heads. Look at the Hopkins group, for example. Popsy Welch and Cushing tried to be smart and thought they were when they became members in good standing of the S.P.C.A., but it availed them exactly nothing. I overheard Cushing say once, "It's better to fight from within than from without," and in a general sort of way that's true, but not with the S.P.C.A. You're never going to convince them of *anything*—from within *or* without. Their minds are made up. It's the other people, the great masses who are not members of the

S.P.C.A. but are influenced by their mouthings and their subtle and not so subtle publicity, that you've got to reach.

Neither Cushing nor Popsy knew how to reach these latter people, and nobody else at Hopkins did either. As a matter of fact, doctors generally don't. Like Popsy and Cushing, most doctors talk down to the ordinary mortal. They don't mean to and mostly they don't think they are when they're doing it. The ordinary mortal is sort of childish in a way and likes nothing better than to be told human-interest stories. He likes to be kidded, too, and his sense of humor is rather keen. You talk to him about diphtheria and the way you grow the germs that cause it and the antitoxin that has been discovered to cure it, and he is mildly interested but not impressed. But you tell him about little Annie Sumolsky whose old man is a cripple and couldn't run his little grocery store if it wasn't for Mrs. Sumolsky, and she ain't too well either on account she's got the "bronical" pleurisy, and his heart is torn. He'll go to bat for you. Little Annie is only five but she got diphtheria, and old Doc Flaherty gave her a shot of antitoxin which cured her in twenty-four hours. Boy, that's something, and when the neighbors took up a collection to pay for the Sumolskys' drug that they got from the great big hospital near by, the story is better still, and what chance would the S.P.C.A. have against that? What if the doctors did have to use a few cats and dogs to make the drug? G'wan.

Well, dear old Popsy and his erudite mates couldn't sound off like that. All they could do was talk in elegant language—using simple words if the people would read them, which they wouldn't—and all the while the enemy kept knocking away at the Hunterian. They arrested boys and men who brought in dogs, whether they were stray dogs or not, and they prevented the Hospital from getting animals from the pound. The pound might have a hundred or even more dogs that were to be put to death in some painless way, but not one of them could be sent to the Hopkins for purposes of discovering something to prevent pain, crippling, even the death of countless Annie Sumolskys.

So the fight went on and it didn't only slow up work in the Hunterian Laboratory; it slowed it up in all the laboratories. The

Hunterian was just the gathering place of animals and the place where they were fed and kept against requisition from the different departments. It cost less that way; each department got its allotment or quota, depending on needs and the stock available; and the animals themselves were better off. Special keepers, and I never saw a more decent or humane group, looked after them; the animals (mostly dogs, but some cats; the occasional goat; later, monkeys; also guinea pigs and rats) came to know them and like them, and rarely was there trouble.

From the beginning Cushing was extremely solicitous of the animals and impressed upon everyone that there would be no tolerance of cruelty or careless handling. All work was to be done on the highest scientific plane, and nothing should be done without proper and adequate anesthesia; problems had to have sense and reason; they all were to be properly supervised; any authorized person (doctor or not) was welcome to make investigation. In the case of surgical procedures the same aseptic technique as that of the general operating room was to be used to the minutest detail—anesthetic, face masks, sterile gowns, sterile sheets, towels, the usual hand scrub-up, sterile rubber gloves, the skin preparation of the animal similar to that of the human, instruments, and, finally, dispatch in operation. Shock, if it came, hemorrhage, if encountered, were to be handled in the usual manner, and many is the animal that had watchful care for hours, including blood transfusion, before being gently taken to its cage. And if you don't think doctors and attendants didn't miss lunches and dinners, if you think they didn't stay up all night long plenty of times tending their charges, you know little of high-grade experimental medical work as it is done in well-ordered, well-organized laboratories.

Cushing did more. He let it be known that sick and injured pets would be treated by himself and staff gratis, and in course of time loads of people lost their fear of the Hopkins laboratory and brought their pets in for treatment and operation. Many animals came from distant parts. No one was charged, but if a person wished to make a contribution it was not refused. I was offered fifteen cents once by a boy of eight whose dog had been in a fight and came out second best.

"Hadn't you better keep that, sonny?" I said.

"Nope. I saved it up an' you fixed up Mike. My Mom says Mike's bin in too much trouble an' if it's gonna cost me sumthin' to have him fixed up maybe I'll try harder to keep him out of more." He grinned. It was sound reasoning, and the Hunterian became the richer by fifteen cents.

So, one way or another, friends were made. But it didn't help. Nothing helped, and when things got too hot and it looked as if the S.P.C.A. was about to have its way with the State Legislature and outlaw animal experimentation completely, there was nothing to do but mobilize the whole medical profession and descend on Annapolis. This happened regularly every few years. Dr. Welch and Dr. Cushing and all the other great lights from the Hopkins herded the group together. I don't seem to recall Dr. Halsted going along or ever becoming personally vocal, but it was generally understood that he was with us in spirit, and, as you might suspect, the whole success or failure of the mission depended on Popsy anyhow. Other men could talk and argue. Highly regarded, well-beloved practicing physicians could tell of the miracles wrought by things that had come from laboratories and be listened to with respect, but it was always the little rotund man with the twinkle in his eye and the extraordinary flow of words who clinched matters. He it was who spoke the magic word—and in every instance kept the laboratories open.

Sounds ridiculous, doesn't it? Yet it still goes on and not only in Maryland but in New York, and other places, too. If the people only realized that you can't stop scientific investigation. If it can't be done one way, it will be done another way. Ever hear of the days of body snatching for purpose of dissecting? It's the same thing with animal experimentation. Either you do it legally and decently and with control, or you have it done *sub rosa* and entirely uncontrolled.

And I don't say this because I did such work and had some slight success and knew others who had more—some who made great discoveries. I say it because it is the only way and the safest. How could Dr. Abel, who experimented so much with new and untried chemicals, know whether the substance he was working with was dangerous to life unless he tried it on something that had life? And who would want trial made on a human? How could evaluation be made of all these recent miracle things like sulfas and penicillin except through animals? It's bad enough and plenty costly when the limits of animal trial have been reached and transfer to the human is in order.

I remember well the agony some of us went through when the time came for that, and "agony" is the word. Take the one item of blood transfusion that everybody nowadays looks upon as commonplace—as indeed it is. But as short a time ago as 1908 it was anything but that. In fact, it wasn't done successfully in Baltimore at all. Then came animal experimentation and with it a tube perfected in Cushing's laboratory that worked smoothly, beautifully on the dog and took but a scant twenty minutes to do. It took *seven hours* in the first human case, used up two donors, and all but killed one. (We bled him too much.) Not only that, the great and nationally known surgeon, John M. T. Finney, was demoted from first assistant in favor of a Hopkins third-year student because the one had not had experience on dogs and the other had! Talk about agony. The doctors who took part in that historic case sweated more blood than donors lost or the patient received. He lived.

And then came the second case—also successful but again something terrible. Only one donor was needed and the time was cut two-thirds. Donor and patient (a doctor, by the way—leukemia) had to lie side by side on adjacent operating tables and an actual connection between the blood vessels of their arms had to be made. That was difficult enough, but worst of all was the fact that there was no way of measuring or knowing how much blood was being pumped from the giver to the receiver. Think of it, you who in these enlightened days have lain down on a couch midst pleasant, quiet surroundings and had a nurse merely insert a needle in your vein, take an exact amount of blood, thank you, and go her way with a smile. All we could do was guess and look for signs—how the receiver was improving in color and pulse rate and blood pressure, and how the other guy was sinking. And some people object to animal experimentation!

And then came the third case. A woman whom we killed outright—then and there—in two minutes. All because we had no precedent, didn't know and didn't even suspect—couldn't, in fact, even with animal experimentation. A dog's heart is strong and can take a beating from high-pressure inflow, but the sick human being's heart isn't and can't. Sure, you're right, we might have suspected it, but what with making the hookup and all the other hundred and one things going on in an operating room at an early trial of something brand new, we didn't. Talk about agony. Talk about being crushed yourself. Talk about . . . well, now you know why some of us fellows haven't so much patience with people who insist upon remaining blind when there is so much light.

It's as I say, though. The doctors never were smart. They never could see the great value of taking the people into their confidence— whether it be animal experimentation, medical procedure, anything —and they don't now. Just suppose, for instance, that visitors were encouraged to come and watch experimental work. I don't agree that they'd get in the way or impede things. Just suppose laymen of intelligence—women as well as men—could have come and watched Halsted or Cushing actually at work and had them or their associates explain things. Think what it would have meant to them and their friends and acquaintances, people in general who trusted them. The calm, steady, scholarly Halsted who preferred to spend hours upon hours working on a dog to making great sums of money working on private patients. He was interested in goiter work and made contributions of great value to our knowledge of diseases of that gland. He devised a method of constricting arteries by means of an aluminum band and learned how to cure aneurisms—abnormal dilatations, saccular in character, that were either cured or ruptured and caused death.

And the keen-looking, high-strung Cushing of the chiseled features, so much of whose work on the brain was done on dogs in the Hunterian Laboratory which he founded and loved so dearly. I saw him engaged on the hypophysis, that tiny little stemlike thing that lies almost at the root of the brain and proved so difficult to approach. Tumors of it cause gigantism and other growth abnormalities and troubles of more elusive nature. He had a terrible time, I thought, and often seemed disturbed but never discouraged. Eventually he found out how to deal with it. Why could not others have seen him at work; outsiders, laymen? What harm would it have done? Who knows but that they might have preached the gospel and done untold good. And then there was Walter Dandy who, among other things, first injected air into the ventricles of the brain, thus making diagnosis and localization of brain tumors easier and more certain by X ray and other means.

Or if Halsted's and Cushing's work was too involved for the average mortal to grasp, there was equally important work going on of more elementary nature. I think people would have been much impressed by the experiments in plastic surgery being carried on by Staige Davis and certainly they would have given sympathetic attention to Walter Hughson's work on deafness—whether they understood the details of it or not, as I didn't. They might even have wandered over to MacCallum's and Whipple's department—or been taken there—to observe their various and varied exploits. Whipple, you know, later won the Nobel Prize, and while you could hardly expect the laymen to grasp the intricacies of scientific effort, there is little doubt that they could have gotten some drift of things, together with the intent. And when, later, they heard of tangible results, the very idea of their having seen certain of the formative steps would have given pleasure and comfort. I believe firmly in the people and their good sense. Cushing did, too, of course, but he did not understand how to get down to their level. If he had, if he had had the knack of taking them into his complete confidence, I do not believe he would have had nearly so much trouble with the S.P.C.A. as he did.

Cushing left the Hopkins in 1910 to become Professor of Surgery at Harvard, and except for rare visits and an occasional medical meeting we didn't see him much for some years. He was forty-one years old when he took up his new duties and with his usual energy he put his whole soul into the work. Yet when World War I began he took over a hospital group from Harvard and joined the British long before the United States entered the war. When, however, this latter event happened he was transferred to the American Army and rendered distinguished service.

In the last analysis the measure of a man can be taken from several different angles, depending upon your own viewpoint. Harvey Cushing was much more complex than most men, and his activities in so many different fields give evidence of it. I have touched on several but have said little about the one that I personally lay greatest stress on—the making of men. Harvey Cushing was a true disciple of those other stalwart builders of the Hopkins, and evidence of this is seen in the many doctors—not all neurosurgeons—he trained and inspired. Many of them occupy positions of importance and trust in medical centers throughout the United States and Canada and they are carrying on the work he originated. Some of them have formed a society that bears his name. I count it an honor to have been one of those who absorbed something of his great spirit.

Chapter 12

WALTER DANDY, NEUROSURGEON

WALTER DANDY succeeded Cushing and was more brilliant even than his master. He never reached the high level of broad culture and many-sided interests which distinguished his great predecessor, but far outshone him in the daring and originality of his exploits. I think I remarked that the Hopkins was a lucky institution. Graduate of the Hopkins, intern in charge of the Hunterian Laboratory for a year, assistant resident and resident in general surgery for eight years under Halsted and Cushing, Dandy had a firm foundation on which to build and made the most of it. Interestingly enough, he and Cushing did not always see eye to eye even in the beginning and as the years passed they became less friendly. I do not see why matters of this sort should be hush-hush. They are rather interesting and not at all uncommon. Prima donnas rarely tolerate each other. It is said that Dandy was much upset when Cushing refused to take him along to Boston in 1912—only later to come to the conclusion that it was almost the luckiest break he ever got. I would certainly think so.

I knew Dandy from the day he came to work in the Hunterian Laboratory. A Middle Westerner—he came from Missouri, only child of English-born parents—he looked and acted it, and I had the impression that his manner and downright habit of saying exactly what he thought grated on the dapper, highly cultured Cushing. Dandy had a way of listening but not always taking suggestion and he usually followed his own ideas. He continued that all through life and, though pleasant enough in conversation, didn't mind getting tough in argument. Men—students and doctors—came to recognize his superior capabilities and made allowances for his temperament, but his penchant for the positive could not be said to have endeared him to them. As a surgeon he had few equals, though you occasionally heard it said he was too daring. One could see in that the measure of the man's mind. Only the searchers have the courage to try the impossible—and occasionally achieve it.

Even when he was a house officer Dandy began to do the big things that were to bring him and the Hopkins renown.* With a colleague, Blackfan, he worked out (1913) the pathogenesis of hydrocephalus, thus causing Dr. Halsted to say, "Dandy will never do anything equal to this again. Few men make more than one great contribution to medicine."

How mistaken he was! That was only the beginning, and I personally think his work (1918) in ventriculography was greater than the other. This was the injection of air into the brain cavities for localizing brain tumors. Whereas by previous methods only one-third could be localized, now practically all of them could. Think of it. Think, too, of the mind that could conjure up this and other wonderful advances in all but rhythmical order. I couldn't begin to mention all the things he did, but one of his last was the so-called "slipped disk" of the vertebral column that we hear so much about these days. Dandy was the first to operate for it, and many are the painful backs that have been relieved thereby.

Walter Dandy literally worked himself to death, and that, too, was in character. As Firor says, he had an incessant and sustained energy. They tell a story about him to the effect that he used to ride from Baltimore to Chicago—and back—when he wanted a good night's rest. The rocking of the train soothed him and he could think clearly. It was said that some of his best writing was done on the train—let alone good sleeping. The "doctor's disease"—coronary thrombosis—cut him down in 1946 at the early age of sixty, and even that is interesting in that it could only have happened to a doctor. In anybody else the premonitory symptoms of coronary occlusion would have been recognized and not misinterpreted. He was on vacation in Florida and, if I remember correctly, two or three of his eminent colleagues were with him. Rumor has it that they did not take the vague chest and abdominal discomfort seriously, and, of course, he didn't. Thus he didn't lay off work when he got back—not, that is, until more ominous and unmistakable signs appeared! The end was unexpected and sudden.

* Firor, Warfield M., "Walter E. Dandy," *Annals of Surgery*, July, 1947.

In the not too distant future his biographer will recite in detail Walter Dandy's achievements. They will be monumental and startling. He did not quite reach his sixtieth birthday, but if he had, the following tribute (see Firor's article) which had been prepared would have been given him:

In every field of human endeavor there is occasionally one individual whose achievements set him apart from all his predecessors and above all his contemporaries. Often there is no appreciation of his accomplishments during his lifetime, and it is left for posterity to acclaim his work. Sometimes, however, the importance of the man's achievements are recognized and some expression of appreciation is given him. This testimonial is such an expression of appreciation, and is given to Dr. Walter E. Dandy in recognition of his accomplishments in the field of neurosurgery. It can be said in all truthfulness that his contributions to this subject are greater than those of any other person. It is fitting, therefore, that the occasion of Doctor Dandy's sixtieth birthday be celebrated by his friends, who give him this portfolio as an enduring emblem of their loyalty to him and of their recognition of his incomparable achievements. at the Johns Hopkins Hospital.

The Hopkins will wait a long time before it sees another Walter Dandy.

Chapter 13

PHIPPS PSYCHIATRIC CLINIC

As you might suppose, it was Dr. Welch who decided that the Hopkins should have a psychiatric institute. Like a lot of other Americans, lay as well as professional, he seems to have been considerably shaken by Clifford Beers's autobiography, *A Mind That Found Itself*, and decided to act. The lowly state of medical care and attention accorded the mentally ill was probably no lower then than it is now, only Dr. Welch had not had it forcefully called to his attention. The time was 1908, and as he cast his eye about for one or the other of America's ubiquitous millionaires, it lighted upon Henry Phipps, noted Pittsburgh ironmonger, and presto! the deed was done. Johns Hopkins became the proud possessor of the Henry Phipps Psychiatric Clinic, first of its kind in America.*

A large, beautifully appointed structure, it stands majestically in the Hopkins quadrangle of buildings and is one of the most cherished and important of the institution's divisions. For the first time in America mentally disturbed patients could be hospitalized without the usual stigma attached. They simply went to the Hopkins Hospital. Nothing more; nothing less. Once there they went to the Phipps, but that was not the same as going to an out-and-out, well-known, separate and distinct institution for mental ills, and I think the advantage was not to be minimized. Not all mentally ill people are distraught, unruly, out of their minds. Some of them would pass the closest scrutiny of all but experts—and did during the late war and the one before it. These and others very naturally objected to "being put away," as the saying goes—even temporarily— for study or for observation. Their relatives were not always pleased about it, either. You can thus see what a happy solution the Phipps at Hopkins was. Even when it came to be known generally as the mental division of the Hopkins it carried much less of a stigma than the usual asylum or private rest home.

* I have given the reference to *William Henry Welch*, written by Simon Flexner and his son, but wish again to note my great indebtedness to it.

102

From the beginning it was pointed out that the Phipps was not to be just another hospital for the insane. It was to be an institution for the observation, study, and treatment of certain mental ills, with research and teaching its main objectives. Cases that were accepted and found to be beyond aid were transferred to the usual institutions. This policy was not always understood, and in more than one instance I have heard unjust criticism made. Free as well as private cases were accepted and, as usual, patients came from all over the country.

Adolph Meyer was the first Professor of Psychiatry and he built up a formidable staff with the usual residents—Hopkins system and all. He had the laboratories, wards, private rooms, and all at his disposal, and students from the Medical School began having regular work and instruction in dispensary and wards. Scientist, idealist, he soon made himself felt at Hopkins, and though he was not the most inspiring teacher there was no doubt of his sincerity and deep understanding of his subject. There was no doubt, either, of the urgent need for instruction and research into the various phases of mental disturbances. Students and staff alike availed themselves of the opportunities provided by the Phipps, and so did the community at large. Dr. Meyer was glad to cooperate with local agencies, and no little of the success the Phipps Clinic has had stems from his broad conception of social relations. Certain members of his staff have made significant contributions of a practical and scientific nature and their influence has been widespread. Like other Hopkins professors, Dr. Meyer built men.

So much for the blurb. A lot of people know the Hopkins has some sort of institute for mental ills, but you rarely hear them talk about it as they do about other divisions. Most illuminating of all, the students have little to say about it. I lay great stress on this because the Hopkins medical student is no mean reflector of opinion. In fact, he's a very decided personage—I'm including the girls, of course—and is most onto himself. Now more than ever. They have a students' and interns' association, branch of a national group, and that, together with the youth upsurge of recent years, has had influence, but the thing goes deeper than that. The Hopkins medical student is a more serious-minded individual; he is not only well prepared for his work, he has given serious thought to it and other things connected with it. Moreover, he does his own thinking. You can't push him around.

I've always found him tolerant, exceedingly polite, willing to listen, anxious to learn—also ready to laugh; rarely stuffy; with a decided sense of humor—but too much inclined to the scientific viewpoint for his own good. This latter, of course, is but the reflection of the men who teach him, and the Medical School's general tendency. Being a hard-bitten practicing surgeon, who never knew too much about science and was aware of its pitfalls, I long ago constituted myself a "one-man army" at the Hopkins to tell the students the facts of life and warn them away from too much science.

"You guys better remember," I've often said to them, "to think of the common thing first when trying to make a diagnosis."

"Why so, Doctor?" one of them chirped up, with a smile.

"Because that's what your patient, whoever he is, will probably have." And then I went on. "Here at Hopkins you see too much of the rarer stuff, and that gives you false ideas. All these other erudite staff men hammer that into you, and you get to be hell on wheels with aleukemic leukemias, aplastic anemia, and a lot of other such stuff, only you don't know anything about common colds and ingrown toenails and ordinary stomach ache. Yet it's these latter things that most people have—seventy to eighty per cent of them maybe."

The students looked worried, and I went on. "The rarer things come to us at Hopkins in greater than normal proportion because we're big shots." That always got a laugh, occasionally a Bronx cheer! "And, of course, you do have to learn about them. But you do not have to learn about them exclusively, and if I can help it, you won't. The average Hopkins student is so steeped in science that if you touch him he literally squirts it." That, too, always amused them, but they knew it was true.

So I always went my way teaching curbstone surgery, and since the Hopkins was a free country in so far as a man's teaching was concerned, nobody ever even so much as hinted that I was not hand-ing out the exact "Hopkins line." They used to kid me about it, but no one ever suggested that I desist. I even got the impression—vague, intangible—that some of them thought it wasn't a bad idea. It sort of took the curse off the boys and girls. I did teach surgery, of course—the practical stuff—but it was amusing to interlard other things—sometimes very extraneous. I once spent a whole hour giving a wonderful (!) disquisition on professional baseball. Why not? You can't be a good doctor if you don't know baseball. Not in these United States you can't.

So, as I say, I went my way with the students and had a wonderful time. But I never could understand their failure to play up the Phipps, because that especially was scientific in approach. Yet they always seemed interested in the practical psychiatry that I tried to inculcate. I didn't think they knew much about it, but who does? I just happened to be interested because the human approach, the social, the personal, all came to loom large in my conception of illness—surgical as well as medical. And as the years passed, and society became more and more complex, this phase took on added significance. In all my work, in all my instruction, I stressed it and lost no opportunity to get it across to my charges.

"In practical medicine above all," I said, "you've got to combine common sense with science—only when it comes to the mental angle of ills we in medicine do not seem to have sufficient knowledge." There was usually silence at that sally. "That's why, I suppose, the psychiatrists seem to get such poor results with the cases we turn over to them. Too, many of them are short on practical knowledge and not too long on the scientific. I had thought the Phipps would change all that."

Questions would follow, and some discussion, but they didn't seem to play up the Phipps. I thought it strange—and still do.

When Dr. Meyer reached seventy he retired. His successor is Dr. John Clare Whitehorn, and I have no doubt that under him the Phipps will take on added importance in the Hopkins ring. It should. Of all medical knowledge I think we are weakest in that concerned with the mind. If the two great wars the world has just come through have taught anything, it is that the world of tomorrow will be different in many respects from that of yesterday—even that of today. Unless I miss my guess it will be a very unhappy one unless the Phipps and other psychiatric institutions are accorded every possible aid. I don't fear the infections, I don't fear even cancer so much as I do the influence of minds gone wrong.

Chapter 14

PEDIATRIC CLINIC

The pediatric division of the Hopkins is the Harriet Lane Home for Invalid Children. It had its own endowment with its own trustees, but through mutual agreement arrangements were made to erect a suitable building in the Hopkins quadrangle. This occurred in 1910, since which time it has been an integral part of the Hopkins Hospital and Medical School. It was sorely needed, and not alone for the special study of children's diseases that has been so ably conducted within its walls. It isn't good for children to be scattered here and there in surgical and medical wards for adults—as in the beginning had been the custom at the Hopkins—and what with the various affections peculiar to childhood isolation as well as treatment they presented difficult problems. The Harriet Lane Home was an acquisition of high importance.

Von Pirquet, noted pediatrician of Vienna, was in temporary charge for a year, and it was hoped he would remain but he chose to return to his native land. John Howland ably succeeded him but he died all too soon, and then came Edwards A. Park—from Yale. The year was 1927, and it is generally conceded that with his coming pediatrics became a more vital force at Hopkins. This isn't said in disparagement of his predecessors, but medicine generally was just then undergoing the transition that was to reach unheard-of scientific heights, and Park played a considerable role in the field of pediatrics. The newly discovered vitamins, among other things, began to assume high importance in the child's metabolism, and the scientific achievements of Park in conditions of the bone, scurvy, and other affections were impressive. Added to that was a clinical ability not usually found in one so thoroughly saturated with the scientific—to say nothing of charm of manner and personal magnetism—and you had the perfect setup. Doctors and patients alike flocked to the Harriet Lane Clinic, and both were rewarded. Once again the Hopkins had found its man.*

* Dr. Park reached the age of retirement (seventy) a year or so ago and

The fact that Park was on full time and had never engaged in private practice seemed to make no difference to him, the sick, or to clinicians generally—which all goes to prove that in the last analysis when it comes to medicine it is more a question of the man than the system. Park's chief activities were in the Hopkins Hospital, but he did go to other institutions, even to the home, upon occasion, for consultation and always was able to see things in practical as well as scientific light. More than one hard-bitten clinician was heard to make favorable comment, and when I tell you that the doctor was a whimsical, soft-spoken type of man who—in the manner of Halsted—sometimes liked to sit and indulge in philosophical speculation that wasn't always clear to the other fellow, this was praise from on high indeed.

One member of Park's staff has received no little acclaim these recent years. Dr. Helen B. Taussig, Hopkins graduate, was always much interested in congenital anomalies of children's hearts, and from that came the suggestion of the so-called "blue baby operation" * we are at present hearing so much about. In cooperation with Dr. Alfred Blalock, Professor of Surgery and also a Hopkins graduate, an operation was conceived for correcting a birth anomaly that restricted blood flow through the lungs of certain babies. It worked on animals—after much experimentation, of course—and then came trial on humans. The success has been startling, and though the operation requires special training there can be little doubt that it will soon be a routine affair in clinics throughout the world.

I always thought that the Harriet Lane was badly placed in the Hopkins grounds. It is on the off side of the quadrangle—next to Phipps Psychiatric—far removed from the wards of the general hospital, the operating rooms, accident department, and dispensary. It is true that these latter had already been erected, and by the time

---

has been succeeded by Dr. Francis F. Schwentker, a Hopkins graduate in his middle thirties.

* Blalock, A., and H. B. Taussig, "The Surgical Treatment of Malformation of the Heart in Which There Is Pulmonary Stenosis or Pulmonary Atresia," *Journal of the American Medical Association*, 128:188, May 19, 1945.

the Harriet Lane came along there was no other place for it in the grounds than that selected, but why did it have to be an entity, all separate and distinct? I have no doubt its board would have insisted, but I also wonder if the Hopkins people considered putting it on top of one of the other buildings—or perhaps attaching it to one of them, where you could get at it easily.

As it is, the Harriet Lane misses much of the running in and out of doctors—often just to see and have conversation—that has always been one of the chief charms of the Hopkins. I grant that as the institution grows and expands you see less of this than formerly, and maybe in the special case of children they wouldn't want so much of the free and easy visiting, but I doubt it. It's too valuable and important in developing the spirit of investigation, creating interest, making friends, increasing general knowledge, and broadening one's viewpoint. The Harriet Lane runs its own dispensary in its own building—away from the dispensaries of medicine, surgery, orthopedics, genitourinary, *et al.*,—and to my mind that, too, is bad. True, the medical students are in attendance at Harriet Lane during regular periods and receive instruction from pediatricians, but what about consultation with physicians, surgeons, orthopedists, and such, especially the older clinicians?

Sure, they do refer cases from Harriet Lane to these other departments for opinion but they don't send their histories along, and the doctors don't show up, either. Many is the time I personally felt that a word with the doctor who had seen the child in question or had been concerned with it would have been helpful in arriving at conclusions. Many is the time I felt that instruction was faulty or incomplete because the doctor wasn't there or even available. And then there were the out-and-out surgical cases in children or child adults where pediatric advice was desirable, only there weren't any pediatricians. No, however admirable the pediatric clinic at the Hopkins is, I cannot personally feel that the over-all setup is perfect. I am not even certain that it will be when they add to Harriet Lane the contemplated hospital for surgically ill children. Nobody ever asked my opinion, but when they tell me that surgery in general for children requires special surgeons I just wonder.

Maybe at a place like the Hopkins, where the unusual with all their special needs is the usual. Not elsewhere. Even specialization can be overdone.

To those who would argue that the above remarks apply equally well to the Phipps Psychiatry and to the Wilmer Institute for the Eye—both of which are widely separated from the general wards and dispensaries—I would say that they do, but with less emphasis. There isn't the same constant, urgent, important need for consultation in those specialties, nor is there the borderline overlapping comparable to pediatrics and medicine and surgery.

Chapter 15

HUGH YOUNG AND THE BRADY UROLOGICAL INSTITUTE

NEXT TO BE added to the expanding Hopkins was the Urological Institute (January 21, 1915), gift of James Buchanan Brady, erstwhile New York financier of playboy tendencies. Because of a penchant for jewelry bristling with diamonds of all sizes and shapes, Brady became widely known as "Diamond Jim," but whatever his little foibles he did a signal service to humanity. In providing suitable opportunity at Hopkins for development of modern urological surgery in general and the talents of Halsted's blossoming Hugh H. Young in particular, he wrought better, perhaps, than he knew.

Other men had been engaged in the study of male genitourinary troubles before Hugh Young, and considerable advance had been made, but few would deny that it was Young's ingenuity, originality, and deep understanding, chiefly, that provided the much-needed scientific basis. It was more than that. Young had terrific drive and an enthusiasm that kept him always keyed up. He also had a charm and a convincing way that won immediate confidence and attracted adherents. Besides, he became a skillful, resourceful surgeon—an excellent executive, an inspired teacher. Little wonder that he rose to be the foremost genitourinary surgeon in America or that he attracted students from far and wide and built up a new and better generation of surgeons who, for the first time, carried the modern concepts of their specialty to almost every corner of the world.

I dare say Dr. Young will be best remembered for his so-called "perineal prostatectomy" and the unique instruments he devised for facilitating it. True, there was the preliminary treatment required— ofttimes tedious—but there, too, he shone, for he was untiring in developing the technique and carying out the studies needed to bolster damaged kidneys. His own results were startling. Where previously men with prostate gland trouble were compelled to eke out miserable existences—the so-called "catheter life"—they could now be relieved completely and permanently and with an almost vanishing mortality.

The Brady Institute of the Hopkins—too small, too soon—became a mecca for patients and doctors alike, this time from the four corners of the world. It is doubtful if there is a hospital in existence that hasn't felt Hugh Young's influence and, through him, that of the Johns Hopkins.

What makes the Hopkins great, what makes it tick? Well, it was Welch, Osler, Halsted, and Kelly who started it and set the pace and created the aura, but it was the Hugh Youngs who came after them and the Finneys and Harvey Cushings, just to mention some— and the Alfred Blalocks and Helen Taussigs of a later generation. In short, it has been the measure of its men and women, and for various reasons the Hopkins has had more than its share. I think it was the initial idea of individual investigation that was so much in the air that was paying off. It didn't matter who the man was, what department he worked in, what his problem was, they let him alone and gave him his head. Not only that, he was privileged to seek aid wherever he wished, and not necessarily in his own department. Work was thus pleasant, there was no hurry, few questions were asked, and there was no conflict. There was no central agency for registration of one's problem for priority purposes, but it was a sort of unwritten law or gentleman's agreement that one man's work should not be encroached upon by another, whether of his own or another department. I personally never knew of trouble in this direction, which speaks volumes for the friendly spirit prevailing. There was never rivalry or jealousy, and when a fellow hit the jack pot there was universal rejoicing.

Young was really a fabulous character. Like most men of great proportions, he was an arch showman. Not everybody at the Hopkins liked that streak, and there were those who felt that the doctor was in the limelight too much and upon occasion disturbed the restrained culture that was the mark of the institution. Young was not the highly educated, trained scientist to begin with. That came later. As the University of Virginia had scant clinical facilities at the time of his graduation, he went into practice in San Antonio,

Texas, the place of his birth, but soon gave it up. Ambition and the realization of his own deficiencies convinced him that if he was ever going to amount to anything he had best get more education. Thus it was that he came to the Hopkins. The fame of its great men proved the attraction. The year was 1894, the Hopkins Hospital had been open only five years, and Young was twenty-four years old.

He wanted to do surgery and hoped to become one of Halsted's house officers; but since there wasn't an opening there he began working in Dr. Welch's department, where bacteriology became his first interest. In between times he worked in the surgical dispensary under Finney. Luck was with him, though, and when an intern fell ill Young got his place. He seems always to have had a penchant for studies in the genitourinary field, and it was his accomplishments in this line of work that first really called him to the attention of Drs. Welch and Halsted. On November 29, 1897, only three years after he had come to the Hopkins, he was given charge of the Department of Genitourinary Diseases in the dispensary, and from that time on there was no heading him off. He was only an assistant resident at the time and never did become resident, but he seems to have learned enough surgery to get by with, and that was all he needed at the start. About a year after his appointment, he ceased living in the Hospital and went out to practice in the city, making a specialty of his chosen field.

It would be out of place to give here a detailed account of Young's researches and activities, but they were many and varied. He had a talent for invention and devised many different instruments, especially cystoscopes, for facilitating the operations he conceived, but more than that, or perhaps along with it, he perfected better methods of diagnosing kidney and other ailments. One of these methods concerned a dye, phenolsulphonephthalein—abbreviated to phthalein—discovered by Dr. Remsen, Professor of Chemistry at Hopkins (later President), and discarded as useless. In collaboration with Rowntree of Dr. Abel's pharmacological staff and Geraghty of his own, Young put this to use and it became one of the most reliable of all tests—later on being of service in saving its discoverer's life!

But withal, I do not believe Young would ever have reached such heights of success if he hadn't come up with Diamond Jim Brady. He would never have gotten the needed clinical facilities, and without them and the complete independence they gave with their free beds, private beds, X rays, laboratories, diagnostic rooms, and independent resident staff, he could not possibly have attained greatness as he did. At that, though, if it hadn't been Brady it would have been somebody else, for Young had no inferiority complex, and his dynamic quality would never have let him rest till he got what he wanted.

Interestingly enough, the Brady Clinic—opened in 1915—had hardly gotten well organized when Dr. Young characteristically threw it over for service in World War I. And I say characteristically because of the way he did it—with a flourish and a nonchalance and a suddenness and a devil-may-care-let-the-future-go-hang that made people literally gasp. I thought it was wonderful, and being from the wild and woolly West myself understood the call of adventure, but others at the Hopkins didn't. They said it was but another instance of his exhibitionism and flair for show-off and what-in-the-hell good was a professor of genitourinary surgery going to be in France anyhow?

What Young actually did was to wangle his way with one or two associates on the very ship (the *Baltic*) that took the great Commander-in-chief Pershing over. How he did it is recounted in the doctor's autobiography,* and it is a wonderful story even if it is terribly involved and not entirely clear. Somehow or other he had enormous drag and he used it to the full. He says by way of excuse that he had become enraged at the Germans and after having made every effort to compel our country to see things as he and his friends did and face up to realities he just had to go the first moment war was declared. The fact that he and his friends appeared on the *Baltic* in uniform while Pershing and his staff didn't—due to the General's desire for the utmost secrecy—didn't come out till later, but it only makes the story better. Civilian clothes were somehow gotten for them, and, of course, they looked terrible, but according

* *Hugh H. Young: A Surgeon's Autobiography*, Harcourt, Brace & Company, Inc., New York, 1940.

to Young "not much worse than General Pershing and his staff, most of whom looked like tramps."

The time was May 29, 1917, and nobody else in America but Hugh Young would have gotten away with such a thing. As it was, he apparently charmed all with whom he came in contact, including Pershing, and from then on it was smooth sailing for him. He really did do great work in the war, and, of course, the venereal disease problem was of extreme importance. Young was put in charge, and it was through that means and the necessity of his investigating things generally that he did so much traveling and saw so much of the war—more, if you could believe some of his friends, than any other member of the A.E.F.

I wouldn't know about that, but during the very height of the Second Battle of the Marne in mid-July or thereabouts (1918), I came up with him, or, rather, he came up with me at a little front-line hospital for the more serious battle-wounded. It was in the town of La Ferte-sous-Jouarre, not far from Chateau-Thierry. With dying men lying around in tents or out in the open waiting for operation that the four teams of surgeons were hard pressed to give them, the one thing we were not bothered about was venereal disease or affections of the genitourinary tract. Yet who should show up but Dr. Young—full up with stories of the desperate fighting just up ahead which he had been personally witnessing. We were all terribly impressed, and his descriptions were thrilling, but there was work to be done, and we hadn't time to listen at length.

I suppose it was that, together with the bleary-eyed, dragged-out appearance of the little group that finally caught the doctor's attention, and gave him the idea of helping out. You could say one thing of Young, he wasn't afraid of anything, not even work.

Calling me aside in between operations, he said, "Bernheim, you fellows look seedy, and I've just been wondering if I couldn't help out."

"Why, Dr. Young," I said, "that'd be fine. What would you like to do?"

"Why, take a table, of course, and let you or someone else rest."

"But—but—" I started to say, and he forestalled me.

"Yeah, I know what you're about to say. Do I know how to do war surgery? The answer is yes. Don't give yourself any concern, and let's get going."

I was in charge of the shift, and the responsibility was mine, but you couldn't stop Young, and it was a noble gesture. I decided to let him go ahead, but to watch him. I did more than that, though he'd have killed me if it had become known. Whereas all the other surgeons, including myself, were operating on cases as they were put on their tables, regardless of their nature or whether they were easy or difficult—amputations, *débridements*, chests, brains, faces, even occasional abdomens—I went out into the tents and chose the eminent professor's cases and saw to it that they were not too heavy.

He did know enough about war surgery to get by, but not sufficient to give him the ease and speed required for front-line work. In the front-line field hospitals, where every moment counts and the dreadful grueling work never ceases day or night, it is know-how that makes for excellent work, and speed and know-how come only from constant operating. Also, there was the question of physical strength to stand up to it, and that, too, comes only from conditioning—and youth. Hugh Young made a valiant effort but he was terribly slow and, of course, older. The rest of us did two or three operations while he did one. But he kept on and only relaxed when he was physically exhausted.

"Bernheim," he said to me five hours after he had begun, "my back is about to break. I don't see how you fellows stand it."

"Sometimes I don't either, Dr. Young," I replied, "but when there's nobody else to take your place you sort of find a way."

"Yes, I suppose that's it. The folks back home don't know the half of it, do they?"

"No, and I guess it's best that they don't."

He looked pale and drawn, and I admired him. I felt, though, that he should quit and decided to ease him out.

"We're terribly grateful for the help you've given us, Dr. Young. The surgeon whose place you took has had some rest and will take over from you."

Johns Hopkins

The Johns Hopkins Hospital

Photograph by Fabian Bachrach, Baltimore, Md.

William H. Welch

William Osler

William S. Halsted

Howard A. Kelly

Harvey Cushing

John M. T. Finney

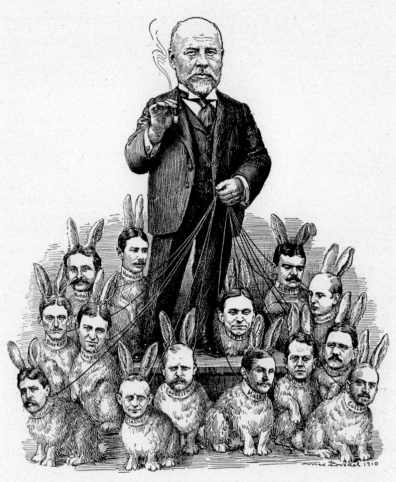

Some Welch rabbits

Cartoon by Max Brödel in honor of Dr. Welch's eightieth birthday.

"That's good. I just wanted to do what I could. I'll be seeing you." And with a wave of the hand and a smile he hopped in his car and off he went. I didn't see him again till we were all back home.

After the war, Young took up his work at the Hopkins where he had left off—Brady Clinic and all—and was more brilliant than ever. As teacher, investigator, administrator, he had few equals and no superiors. Not only that, he knew men, and developed a group of genitourinary surgeons that literally flooded the country. He nurtured them and provided ways and means for their study and later practice, even to setting up their offices, and there were few clinics that didn't have one or more of his men, all well trained, eager, adventuresome—several of them professors or directors in their own right.

I personally regard Hugh Young as one of the Hopkins's greatest men. They say he made huge sums of money and lived the full life, but what of it? He did enough to entitle him to both, and if some of those who criticized him most looked beneath the surface, they would be surprised. He gave freely of his services to the lame, the halt, and the blind. No sick person ever found him callous or unsympathetic, and with the needy the element of money never entered into it. Only his closest intimates knew what vast sums of money he put into his work, the clinic he headed, and the men he developed. Suppose he was a showman. The Hopkins could do with more showmen like him.

Young died in 1945 at the age of seventy-five.

Chapter 16

SCHOOL OF HYGIENE AND PUBLIC HEALTH

THE HOPKINS list of firsts has been long and distinguished. In 1918 it became the first medical institution in America to have a School of Hygiene and Public Health. This school was established by the Rockefeller Foundation and housed in a newly erected structure across the street from the original quadrangle of the Hopkins Hospital. Dr. Welch became its first director, and thus proper organization was insured. When he got it going to his satisfaction he turned it over to Dr. William H. Howell, former Professor of Physiology and Dean at the Hopkins, and it couldn't have fallen into the hands of a better administrator.

There was urgent need in America for a school of this type, and students and doctors began to enroll immediately. It is, of course, a graduate school and it gives its own special degrees. Only to a limited extent does it come within the orbit of the Medical School proper; the medical students have few courses there,* so apparently that was not the reason for establishing the school. The main reason was the paucity of trained health officers necessary for the proper handling of public health problems throughout the nation. It seems that the Rockefeller Foundation's interest in this growing field had been stimulated among other things by the devastating effects of hookworm disease and by the campaign put on to stamp it out—the South being chiefly affected. Health officers of quality and character and training were discouragingly few, and something had to be done about it. Dr. Welch again was consulted, and the Hopkins got the school. It should be noted that Dr. Welch had long been interested in local and general problems of health and sanitation. As far back as 1898 he became a member of the Maryland State Board of Health and served as its president from 1900 to 1922, during which time he inaugurated the first modern health department the state had ever had.

At or about the same time, Harvard was given funds to establish

---

* Biostatistics and epidemiology.

a similar school, and one of my Hopkins colleagues who is not on the School of Hygiene staff told me the following story about the two schools. He said that there was question as to whether a new and separate school should be established or whether the funds should be used to integrate the Public Health and Hygiene Departments into the regular Medical School. Certain departments already going—Physiology was given as an example—would be strengthened, while new and different departments could be added. After due deliberation Dr. Welch and his Hopkins colleagues decided that it would serve all purposes better not to do this but to establish a separate and distinct school. The Harvard authorities followed the first idea and now, twenty-five years or so later, have decided they were mistaken and are in process of establishing a separate and distinct institution as the Hopkins did originally.

A classmate of mine, who later became the school's director, Allen W. Freeman,* tells of the unusual class he faced at his very first lecture, and nothing will give you a better idea of the institution's appeal. Of thirty-seven members, all medical graduates, the nineteen Americans were from fourteen states. The eighteen foreigners—of whom two were women—came from Central Europe, Latin America, Canada, and Asia. Most of the foreign students came on fellowships provided by the Rockefeller Foundation. It wasn't until 1936—through passage of the Federal Social Security Act—that American students in volume began to attend on scholarships provided by our government. The pressing need for health officers had struck home.

It is hardly to be doubted that the authorities of the Rockefeller Institute watched the growth and development of the School of Hygiene at the Hopkins with ardent interest. Men of promise and accomplishment were invited to join the faculty, and it wasn't surprising that the group assembled compared favorably with other Hopkins staffs. In the years that followed, the achievements of Raymond Pearl in vital statistics, W. H. Frost in epidemiology,

* Freeman, Allen W., "Five Million Patients," Charles Scribner's Sons, New York, 1946.

McCollum in nutrition—notably vitamins—and others were much in the news.

One interesting development that has not received the attention it merits from laymen was the "establishment in 1932 of the so-called Eastern Health District, organized as a field study and training area in cooperation with the Baltimore City Health Department and other agencies actively engaged in public health work." * As usual, the Rockefeller Foundation provided most of the funds. The area comprises about a square mile not far from the school, and some one hundred thousand people live within it. Special studies of practical and scientific interest are carried on there, and the staff man in charge is also a health officer of the city. It doesn't require much imagination to understand the extreme value of such field work—carried out, as it were, in the institution's own grounds.

And just of late, through the generous gift of a Baltimorean, Mrs. May McShane Jenkins, a new Department of Biophysics is to be added to the School of Hygiene. At least that is the assumption. I can't say that biophysics means very much to me, but according to the *Baltimore Sun*,† "In announcing the gift, Dr. Lowell J. Reed, vice president of the university, states that it is believed that the Hopkins will perform a unique service if it succeeds in producing investigators capable of advancing biology in terms of physics and mathematics and at the same time extending physics by utilizing the material and mechanisms revealed by recent developments in biology.

"These terms are somewhat difficult for the layman to grasp. Suffice it to say that, as the frontiers of human knowledge are extended, familiar subjects, such as physics, biology and chemistry assume new ramifications, frequently in combination with each other. Further research into them requires the establishment of new departments with the necessary equipment and a personnel trained to do this advanced work. The Hopkins has created a committee on development whose task is to explore the new fields and determine

* Note from School of Hygiene Catalogue, 1947–1948.
† April 26, 1947.

which ones should be established as departments when funds are available.

"Mrs. Jenkins's gift is of great value in enabling the Hopkins to keep abreast of the latest developments in medical research, in which it was a pioneer. Needless to say, the university is prepared to make good use of similar benefactions."

It remains only for me to add that the Rockefeller Foundation has hardly used its funds to better purpose than in establishing the School of Hygiene and Public Health at the Hopkins. One might even venture the opinion that the health and welfare of the world, let alone that of this country, is being significantly affected by its graduates.

Chapter 17

OBSTETRICS. J. WHITRIDGE WILLIAMS

IT WAS the pattern in the early formative years of the Hopkins for men to begin in Dr. Welch's laboratory. Of course by this time you've realized that if one had stuff Dr. Welch quickly found it out, and from then on it was just a question of where he would put him—he being the mastermind.

J. Whitridge Williams is probably not well known to many of this day but he played no inconsiderable role in the Hopkins story. He became the first Professor of Obstetrics, later Dean of the Medical School, and from the beginning was an arch protagonist of the full-time system, a subject which will be discussed in detail in a later chapter. He began humbly in the pathological laboratory, and Dr. Welch put him in obstetrics, or pointed him to it. Actually he started him off in gynecology, under Dr. Kelly, because obstetrics at that time was part of gynecology. This was in 1891, and Williams, graduate of the University of Maryland, knew much more about the pathology of the female organs than he did about gynecology or obstetrics. As a matter of fact, I guess that was why Dr. Welch pointed him to obstetrics. He thought obstetrics needed to be put on a firm scientific basis and chose Williams to do it.

He chose well, and one thing leading to another they cut obstetrics loose from gynecology in 1899 and made Williams Professor with Dr. Kelly's blessing. He had suggested it three years earlier. Williams was a character and had color. Born and raised in Maryland and son of a physician—a blue blood by inheritance—A.B. of Hopkins, and conscious of his social standing, he was nonetheless a gruff, hard-riding, downright man who knew where he wanted to go and went there. I always liked him, and so did lots of others, particularly women, who looked beneath the rough exterior and found an innate charm. They did not, however, miss what a fine figure of a man he was—6 feet 2, athletic frame, good shoulders, fine head—and handsome. As for the others, and there were many, they just plain didn't like him.

He had outstanding ability, and according to those who ought to know, made great contributions to obstetrics in America. He would have no slipshod work about him; his lectures were classics; he gave pathology and bacteriology so you could understand it; he reduced mortality and morbidity; he developed men; and emulating Osler and Howell, he wrote a textbook that went through edition after edition. He was truly a great man.

Like the other professors at the Hopkins of his day, Williams, too, engaged in private practice, but I had the impression he never liked it. He never became the popular obstetrician of Baltimore, but that didn't seem to bother him. He preferred to spend most of his time working at the Hopkins. Naturally he was the number one consultant, and many a "lemon case" was shifted to his broad shoulders. In 1911 he became Dean of the Medical School and kept that position until 1923, when he resigned to devote all his time to placing his department on a full-time basis. It was while thus engaged that he died—after a rather brief illness—in 1931.

J. Whitridge Williams was a tough hombre in many ways. He was familiarly called "the Bull," and a more appropriate name could not have been given him. He gave no quarter and asked none. He was different from most of the other Hopkins men of his day in that he was more direct—less tactful, less bending. You either went his way or no way, and I always wondered how it happened that he made a successful dean. I think it must have been because of his executive ability and deep sympathy and interest in the students. They seemed to sense the charm and kindly spirit under the gruff, somewhat forbidding exterior and got along well with him. Many staff men objected to his dictatorial ways, and when he finally passed on there was not great sorrow. I have to set things down as I think they were.

Williams did his own thinking, and modern obstetrics is all the better for it. He was interested in normal and contracted pelves and made studies on obstetrical hemorrhage, vomiting of pregnancy, Caesarean section, and other things. But time has a way of marching on, and the change in obstetrical procedure is a good illustration. In the good old days at the Hopkins they had an outpatient service in obstetrics that I thought was wonderful, despite the fact that it drove students, doctors, and nurses almost crazy and was sometimes the occasion of much bad language. They've given it up now, but I still think it was wonderful, and for the simple reason that it provided a glimpse of life in the raw and put you on your mettle in a most realistic manner. Realism was one of Whitridge Williams's credos.

We took obstetrics in the fourth year then and each student had to take active part in nine deliveries—either in or out of the Hospital. In order to do that a special room with direct telephone connection was provided in a little old ramshackle rented house directly across the street from the Hospital's main entrance on Broadway. Two students lived there and were on call day and night until their nine babies had come, whether it took two or three or four days or, as actually happened in my case, two weeks. Somehow or other there was a sudden unaccountable dearth of babies when my turn came, and I thought I'd never get off. We didn't expect much of the ward cases because there weren't too many, but the outpatient service was big and active, and the fellows before me had told wild stories about it.

The way it worked was this. Each hospital in the city had a zone to cover, and that of the Hopkins extended for blocks and blocks around—being mostly in the poor white and Negro sections of southeast Baltimore. Pregnant women were supposed to come to the dispensary for registration and examination months before their time and most of them did. No woman in labor was refused, though —that is, whether registered or not—and special grips containing instruments, sterile dressings, and other necessities were kept ready at the Hospital's front office against call. The moment this was received, whether by telephone or by a relative in person, a trained nurse and special intern came and got the grips while telephone operators called the students, and off the cortege set—on foot, of course.

It wasn't so difficult if it was daytime and spring, summer or fall, and not raining. But if it was night, or winter and bitter cold or raining or snowing, it was dismal. The narrow, poorly lighted, roughly paved, tortuous streets and alleys so typical of Baltimore's poorer sections were bad enough, but many of the filthy little homes that reeked of mixed odors—onions, garlic, stale air, fetid sewage —were worse. And when, in addition, there was only candle or lamplight, and you had to go out and buy or scout around for kindling wood to start a fire in a stove that didn't want to cooperate, well, it was something. My babies did begin to arrive, of course— and the stories I'd heard were all true. Never in all my life had I seen such poverty—not even out in the country districts of Kentucky. Sometimes we actually had to shoo children out of the place in order to get things going, and, of course, there was the occasional drunken husband. It was dirty poverty.

The young intern and the young nurse did not make the most experienced obstetrical team imaginable, but the patients were strong and not used to much. I never heard a complaint. The doctor was permitted to use only "low forceps." If anything were needed beyond that or there was unusual difficulty of any kind, he was supposed to call the Hospital, and the patient was promptly admitted by ambulance. None of my cases needed that, and we went gaily on our way making examinations and doing the actual deliveries under supervision and with some little assistance. With the delivery completed we cleaned up the place, saw that mother and child were comfortable, packed up our stuff, left directions and departed. Thereafter for one week it was the student's duty to make daily visits and report back on the *post partum* course.

Only once did we have anything out of the ordinary or did we have an argument—that is, between students and doctor. One afternoon we were called way down to a particularly dismal-looking place, and, believe it or not, when we arrived there was the baby lying naked and uncovered in the middle of the floor, faintly crying —with the mother on a bare mattress in a corner of the room. No attendants, no preparations, nothing. Nothing, that is, but sheer poverty and neglect. I was dumfounded, but the doctor said he had seen it before. The nurse didn't say anything but looked a little sick.

The argument was about credit. My classmate and I wished to know whether the case would count on our list of deliveries.

"Certainly not," said the doctor. "The woman delivered herself, and how can you expect credit for something you didn't do or help in?"

"You're going to examine her, aren't you?" we asked.

"Sure thing."

"And there's the baby—and—and—"

"Go on and get to work and don't be silly. Here, take the baby," picking up the child.

"That's just the point," we said. "We've had a dull time, and the way babies aren't coming it looks like we'll never get off."

"Meaning?"

"No credit—no help. You and the nurse clean up the mess yourselves and be damned. We're leaving."

I still shudder at the thought of what that intern could have done to us. But he was a nice fellow. He's been one of my good friends throughout the years.

"O.K., you win," he laughed. And never did mother and child get quicker or better service, never was a filthy place cleaned up and set to rights in shorter order.

The woman did well, and that case—our fifth—brought us luck because we had four deliveries in the next twenty-four hours. One was in the Hospital and three on the outside, and with one exception that was my entire obstetrical experience. The exception was an emergency delivery several years later occasioned by unavoidable delay in the obstetrician's arrival. I got through it, or rather the baby was born, but it's always been a question of who was the more scared—the mother or I.

As noted, the Hopkins has given up its outside obstetrical service, and that has come about because of the present day hospitalization of expectant mothers. Over 80 per cent of all deliveries the nation over are done in hospitals nowadays, and so the outside need has disappeared. That is the modern trend and it is good medicine, but think what a loss it is to students—a loss, by the way, that cannot be recouped. I would not for one moment think of bringing back the older way; mothers and their babies come first, and more of them will survive under the newer regime; so, too, will there be better doctors. I just say that there was a lot to the human side in yesterday's medicine that we don't see today. In telling my story a nostalgic wave sometimes comes over me. Older graduates of Hopkins will recall Whitridge Williams's refusal to have a modern delivery table in his delivery room.

"You men," he used to say to the students, "will be going out into practice, and since your obstetrics will be done mostly in the homes you will not have the modern delivery tables that can be conveniently adjusted. I therefore prefer to simulate actual conditions here in the hospital. We have an ordinary flat wooden table of the kitchen variety such as you will encounter—if you don't care to use the bed—and I assure you just as good obstetrics can be done on this as on any other."

That was true, of course, but the need has now disappeared. So has Dr. Williams, who went the way of all flesh just at the beginning of the new era.

Nicholas J. Eastman is the new professor and he is a worthy successor to Williams.

Chapter 18

F. H. BAETJER—MARTYR TO SCIENCE

Hopkins had its martyr. Every medical institution of any consequence has one or more. It is one of the sad commentaries of medicine that that has to be. You can't always know in advance how new things will act, what and where the dangers are, and doctors become conditioned to taking chances. Besides which, they are impatient and at times unbelievably careless. Far more than people realize they try things on themselves.

Frederick H. Baetjer, Baltimorean, Hopkins A.B. and M.D. (1897–1901), was the first man at the Hopkins to take up X ray as his life's work. It was in 1902 and while he was still an intern on Dr. Halsted's surgical service. X ray was still in the primitive stage but was becoming especially useful in fractures and bone conditions generally, and the Professor was tremendously interested in it. They didn't have a department for the new field nor did they have an operator of the crude machine. As I recall, it was housed in a little room just off the old surgical amphitheater, and it was from this cubbyhole that Baetjer used to bring out his wet plates for Dr. Halsted and others to look at. He became interested early, was encouraged and permitted to have his head, and thus became an outstanding pioneer—only eventually to lose his life.

I knew "Baetch" well. We had played together on the Hopkins lacrosse team, lacrosse being the one sport the Hopkins always excelled in, and it was there that he excited my admiration—and that of many others. A rather stocky, broad-shouldered, good-looking young man, with pleasant voice and quiet demeanor, he played goal, of all places. I suppose it was his keen eye that contributed so much to his ability—and stood him in such good stead later—but he had highly developed that other quality so essential to a good goalkeeper. He was absolutely fearless. If he couldn't catch a ball in the net of his stick, he'd let it hit him—even in the head. With Old "Baetch" in goal, there was little wonder that we won the championship.

He began his X-ray work in the days when, like the photographers, they used glass plates in lieu of today's films, and when they knew neither the dangers of the rays nor those of the developing fluids. Not only that, even when it began to be noised about by word of mouth and in the medical journals that patients and X-ray operators especially ought to be protected against possible burns, Baetjer first scoffed at it and then took only perfunctory precautions—for himself. He was always meticulously careful about his patients, dosage, and all, and rare indeed was it for one of them to come to grief—none did, so far as I personally know. For himself he said he was too busy to be bothered. You know, the old story of familiarity breeding contempt.

He was good. They used to say that the plates he took were terrible compared to those of the men who followed in his footsteps, but he could see more in them. Even when he lost an eye from a new growth (sarcoma that never recurred) he could still see things hidden from others and make diagnoses from his plates that were positively uncanny. I'm speaking now of X ray years after the beginning, when no part of the body was free from their searching gaze, and medicine as well as surgery was aided. Harry Baetjer had few peers. His fame spread far and wide, and men came to Hopkins from all over to sit at the feet of this great man just as they had to the earlier great lights. His department grew, and he developed a staff—a devoted staff, I should say. Osler, Halsted, Kelly were equally devoted and much impressed.

As was bound to happen, though, the doctor's fingers and hands eventually began to show the effects of the rays and the developing fluids—redness that didn't disappear and then a bit of swelling, followed by small areas of ulceration here and there, mostly at the tips of the fingers. You couldn't argue with Baetjer, and, worst of all, he liked to do his own work. They provided him with lead screens and they gave him assistants and technicians, and it wasn't necessary for him personally either to take the plates or to develop them. But he liked to do both, especially if the case looked interesting and he was in a hurry to see the result. For long years he couldn't bring himself to remain behind the screens the way he should have. Moreover, he'd often "forget" to put on the big rubber gloves provided to protect his hands from the fluids. Most lovable fellow, but stubbornly careless.

Need I go further? The little ulcers healed and then broke down; healed and broke down again—got larger and angrier. The abuse continued in spite of much pain. Then cancerous degeneration, and one operation after another. Excisions of ulcers, skin grafting by Staige Davis, amputations of tips of fingers, amputations of whole fingers. Always more advance. Removal of glands higher up. The doctor kept the surgical staff busy and uneasy—yet he went cheerily on his way, smiling, never complaining, always busily engaged. He developed a huge private practice in X rays.

I was on the sidelines mostly. The older, better surgeons did the operations. But not all the dressings. He used to come down to the dispensary for me to do an occasional one and then he'd sit and rehearse our old lacrosse days. We used to laugh and joke, and I knew what relief it gave him. He had a wonderful sense of humor and liked nothing better than to chide me for certain little weaknesses.

After one particularly good session he said, "You know what, Bernie? You sure could trip up a guy, couldn't you?"

"Well, now—"

"And," with a wide grin, "the way you'd stop suddenly while running and let a fellow run on to the end of your stick!"

"Are you insinuating that I was a dirty player?"

"We-ell," he drawled, "not exactly, but when I die I ain't so sure I'll be seein' you where I'm goin'."

I couldn't help laughing.

"Which way're you goin', Baetch?" I asked.

"Up," he replied. "S'long."

That was the only time I ever heard him even hint at dying. He was just over his fortieth or so operation, as I recall, and we all knew he couldn't take much more. He died shortly afterward—in 1933, at the age of fifty-nine, and the Hopkins lost one of its unexpendables.

Chapter 19

MAX BRÖDEL. JOHNS HOPKINS AND THE MAGIC FORMULA

THE HOPKINS had a positively uncanny knack for getting the right man for the right place. By now you've undoubtedly noticed it for yourself, but it was never better illustrated than in the case of Max Brödel, who wasn't a doctor at all but an artist. A young man of twenty-four, who had been free-lancing in fine art and anatomical and physiological illustrations, Brödel is understood to have been brought over from his native Leipzig in 1894 by Dr. Kelly,* and that too is a good illustration of what was happening in those early days. Hopkins men were constantly wandering about Europe, studying and looking around for talent, and one way or another everybody seems to have met everybody else. I have remarked upon some of these meetings, but now comes another. Brödel met Mall. He had been working in the Anatomical Institute of Leipzig under the famed His, Braune, and Spalteholz, and later in the Physiological Institute under Carl Ludwig. It was in this latter place that he came up with Franklin P. Mall in 1888. They became friends, and it is hardly to be doubted that Mall had much to do with Brödel's early training in anatomy. That both of them would one day become world-renowned in their respective spheres and at the Johns Hopkins probably did not occur to them, but it so happened. Indeed, at the time of their meeting I doubt if they had even heard of the Hopkins.

Thus the search for men to staff the Hopkins was constantly going on in odd corners of America and Europe with increasing rewards. But whether it was Osler or Cushing or Flexner or Brödel, even Dr. Welch, I don't think it was the man himself who did the job entirely. I mean the job of making himself great. The institution

* Two other artists of superior ability were brought over to the Hopkins after Brödel: Herman Becker in 1895, and August Horn in 1898. It would be pleasant to record their contributions, but space doesn't permit, and they are not necessary to the story.

had a lot to do with it, and also the environment, the associations, the way they all lived together in those early days there in the big main building of the new Hospital and talked and exchanged ideas. We tend to lose sight of this today, but those of us who served during the two wars and through necessity lived the life of hospital residents again—somewhat older, more mature men who had only the work in hand to do and plenty of time to talk and explore each other's minds once again—will understand best what I mean. Men aren't developed solely by their own efforts. It is a complex thing that does it: stimulation, example, opportunity and timing, a lot of things, though always there must be a basic quality of character and mind in the man himself. The Hopkins somehow seemed to excel in getting the proper type of mind; and its being able to supply the rest created as it were the "magic formula."

Max Brödel is a shining example. Though he wasn't a doctor he became a resident at the Hopkins Hospital. That in itself was unusual and a terribly smart thing to do regardless of the reasons, *i.e.*, whether he had no other place to live, or they hadn't the money to put him up elsewhere, or they regarded the work he was to do important enough. It placed him immediately on a par with the doctors, and since many of them, like Cushing, Bloodgood, and others who were residents at the time were his own age, of equally charming personality and eager of mind, what more natural than that they should become fast friends and begin exchanging ideas? The fact that Brödel had had a fundamental training in music as well as art and was a superior pianist—almost of concert proportions—added enormously to his popularity. The tones of his brilliant playing used to reverberate through the corridors of the big building, often causing people to loiter and listen at the base of the big marble statue of Christ standing in the main rotunda. I seem to recall it sometimes of a late afternoon, at others in the evening, when men's minds are fogged, and music brings surcease and musings. I was not a resident. I was just one of those who were passing through and listened.

Max Brödel became one of Hopkins's immortals. He brought every ounce of his superb artistic ability to bear and he studied anatomy and surgery as only a man of great intellect could. He became a scientist and actually did investigative work of high quality on the kidney—Brödel, who was not a doctor. Little wonder that his drawings were beautiful to behold and anatomically, surgically, scientifically accurate to the nth degree. Never before had medicine, had the world seen such a thing—either in black and white or in color, for he did both. And they were by no means gross things; they were microscopical, too, for Brödel's skill and knowledge also included the cellular that could only be seen through the high-power microscope. Thus he gave doctors the most beautiful, the most perfect illustrations of operative procedures, and not only that, for the first time men could see gross specimens as well as the microscopical in the texts of pamphlets and books.

Can you see what this meant? Can you see what a grand thing it was—how busy doctors could read and study and learn as never before? Literally it was a metamorphosis. Art as applied to medicine was made into a living, vibrant thing. Books and articles that came from the Hopkins after Brödel got there were the cynosure of all eyes. One hardly had to read the texts, so vivid were the illustrations. Little wonder inquiries began to come in for the privilege of working with him, for his services, from all parts of the world. Yet withal, Brödel remained the same jolly, friendly, hail fellow well met as always—simple of taste, humble, demanding little, giving much. He became a figure of importance not only at the Hopkins but throughout Baltimore and the United States.

Then he received an offer to go elsewhere. Rumor had it that the Mayo Clinic wanted him, and that he could name his own price. Hopkins was put on the spot, but I have the impression that Brödel didn't want to leave, and money was never of too great importance in his life. He had married a lovely girl, an artist and musician like himself and, incidentally, one of his own collaborators and pupils, and they had a family. Through the activities chiefly of Dr. T. S. Cullen,* Dr. Kelly's successor and devoted friend of Brödel,

* Cullen, T. S., "Max Brödel: 1870–1941: Director of the First Development of Art as Applied to Medicine in the World," *Bulletin of the Medical Library Association*, 33:5–29, 1945.

the Hopkins got up a fund for the establishment of the first "School of Art as Related to Medicine." It was to be part and parcel of the Hopkins, Brödel was to be the first Professor and have his own staff. Thus the day was saved, and, as one man remarked, Brödel gave up the chance for wealth and security for a somewhat precarious salary of $5,000 and life at the Hopkins. I don't think he ever regretted it, and certainly the school—first of its kind ever to be established in the United States or elsewhere—stands as a living monument to his greatness. Artists go out from it to every institution of importance throughout the land.

Toward the end, W. B. Saunders Company of Philadelphia, so many of whose medical publications had been featured by Brödel's illustrations, gave him a dinner. It was a unique tribute of appreciation and gratitude, and educators in medicine, as well as many prominent figures not of the medical world from far and near, were invited. The large group from Hopkins went over to Philadelphia in a private car—Max with us—and after a banquet of the finest delicacies—champagne and other wines to suit all palates—the speaking began. You never heard such tributes of affection and admiration, all richly deserved. Max Brödel was a true pioneer in a new field. He died in 1941, but his influence will live forever. Didn't I say the Hopkins produces the magic formula?

Chapter 20

SUPREME COURT FOR DIAGNOSIS. AMERICANA.
THE HOPKINS AND THE MAYO CLINIC

It is not surprising that the Hopkins Hospital very early made appeal to doctors and the sick—distant as well as local—and that the appeal was out of all proportion to the institution's age and maturity. You can't have unusual superiority in anything without its soon becoming known, and in medicine particularly people are keenly alert to new and different procedures, high deeds, and scientific excellence.

One thing they always stressed at the Hopkins from which they brooked no slightest deviation, and that was respect and consideration for all who came to the hospital, regardless of their station in life, the character of their illness, their wealth, their creed, their color. The Negro woman was draped for pelvic examination in the same manner as the high society matron, and no man dared make the examination unless a trained nurse was in attendance. The smelly, the dirty, the loud, nervous ones, prostitutes, cutthroats, ladies, the tough guy, the intoxicated or near-intoxicated, the child with worms or a sore toe, the scalded, the leprous, the injured, those who could and did pay, those who could and didn't, those who couldn't and didn't, the stupid, the intelligent, the wise guys—one and all were welcomed and given the best the institution had, and it didn't matter if they came in at the front entrance on Broadway or through one of the other entrances. It didn't matter, either, if they were Baltimoreans or hillbillies from West Virginia or Kentucky, or natives of North Carolina, or gypsies from the high roads, or big shots from New York, Chicago, Galveston, Mexico, or China. Come one, come all, they got what the Hopkins had, and if they sometimes failed to get the results they expected, it wasn't because sincere effort wasn't made.

The Hopkins Hospital soon became a veritable crossroads, where every variety and degree of disease was seen. For years there was a great deal of typhoid and malarial fever in and around Baltimore.

135

The wards were filled, and I can still hear Dr. Osler's chant about fingers, food, flies, and filth, the four F's that give rise to typhoid. There was pneumonia aplenty, only since we didn't have the sulfas and penicillin the death rates were higher than today. And, of course, there was syphilis, primary, secondary, and tertiary, with only mercury, by inunction and other ways, as the chief means of therapy. The sequelae of syphilis abounded, notably aneurisms, in which Halsted was much interested from the surgical standpoint and Osler from the medical. Heart disease was the same commonplace it still is, and there were nervous affections of all kinds, as well as rare and common skin diseases, and loads of the acute things. Doctors from near and far sent in gall bladders, cancers, goiters, breasts, and sometimes came along with their patients to see how they were being handled and to meet the new institution's great men, attend their clinics and ward rounds, and return home to spread the gospel of their great lore.

It was all grand and glorious, and one could not escape the underlying culture and elegance of the place. It gave the impression of a very high-class club of gentlemen with an undercurrent of good form. It was so real you could more than sense it; you could almost touch it. Yet there was informality in clinics, in teaching, on ward rounds, and at medical meetings, with good fellowship and cooperation. In short, there was a most delightful atmosphere at the Hopkins. The aura was unmistakable.

One thing became clear and it has always persisted. Each professor was head and supreme in every way, shape, and form in his own department, and there was no overlapping. There was friendship and comradeship, respect and admiration. Consultation and advice were asked and freely given, but no man in any department had the slightest thing to say in another department. Moreover, there was never criticism from department to department—not even by the underlings. Not all departments were run equally well, but that was due to the fact that not every professor was a good executive. In a general sort of way, though, there was similarity, and it was seen chiefly in the house officer system. Each clinical department had its own interns, assistants, and chief resident, and each department head kept his resident on for years. This was especially true of Osler and Halsted, and, as I have noted, appointment to their top position was tantamount to eventual professorial appointment elsewhere, because hospitals and medical schools of the day were on the lookout for just such men.

This was the age when doctors of the better training did not abound as they do today. Today you will find good doctors in every town and village of the United States—even sometimes at the crossroads—and there are loads of high-grade medical schools, some sixty-six in all. But in those days the better medical schools were few, and one could almost count them on the fingers of one hand. Good doctors, surgeons, physicians, pathologists, and scientists were to be had, but chiefly in the larger cities and medical centers. Occasionally a smaller city would have an outstanding doctor; and upon rare occasions you found one in the very small center or even out in the wilds of the country. It was not, however, the rule, and hospitals other than those in the cities were manned chiefly by doctors of mediocre ability and accomplishments.

This was especially true of surgeons, and so it happened that Halsted's men were always in demand. True, they did not go to the smaller centers; they did not have to. Even some of Halsted's assistant residents got very good positions. While not the finished product like the resident, many of them had great ability and were quite capable of propounding the Halsted methods. The same was true of Osler's men and Kelly's men. They were in great demand and had a wide variety of choice. And not only was this true in the clinical departments, it was also true in the scientific departments. Dr. Welch's men became outstanding scientists and heads of great scientific laboratories. Dr. Mall's men in anatomy * were called to head anatomy departments elsewhere, and the same was true of Dr. Howell's men in physiology, and Dr. Abel's men in

---

* I should think they were selected for their scientific accomplishments rather than practical knowledge of anatomy. I have wondered whether they followed the precepts of their master in not giving instruction in their subject. It could hardly be that any other institution than the Hopkins would tolerate such a thing.

pharmacology. It was an era, in short, of high demand for men of fundamental training and real accomplishments.

So the magic names were clicking in a big way—so big that it became *de rigueur* for people to come to the Johns Hopkins for review of their ills, general checkup, consultation, advice on medical projects. In short, the Johns Hopkins became the Supreme Court of American medicine. There had been no Supreme Court prior to this, despite the fact that medical centers of quality had existed for some time. They were mostly one-man affairs with a big-name surgeon or physician at the head—John B. Murphy, master surgeon, of Chicago, for example—or they were places like Harvard or Columbia or Pennsylvania where the long-time reputation of the university overshadowed their medical departments and obscured much of their high-grade work and achievements. Nothing of the kind pertained to the Hopkins, even though it, too, was a university. It was too young and, other than the Department of Medicine, was known to comparatively few people and, at that, chiefly for the excellence of its Graduate School. In other words, the great masses were not particularly interested in the Johns Hopkins until its medical men and its new and grand Hospital and its unique Medical School—with women admitted on a par with men—began to make the headlines.

Instantly the place caught the popular fancy. The very name Johns Hopkins was unusual—with that "s" tacked on to the "John." A new star had risen in the nation's medical firmament, a new and different star. Research, investigation, higher medical education were in the very air, and, of course, new and better understanding of ills with perfect diagnoses and sure cures! Periodicals, newspapers big and little carried the news, and people everywhere drank in the glad tidings. I'm only giving you the picture as I saw it unfold, and part of that unfolding appeared to me before I ever came to Baltimore and the Hopkins—when, in fact, I was still a boy in my teens out in Kentucky. I read extravagant stories myself and heard people talking of it without knowing or understanding the meaning or portent.

The whole affair was strange in that there was no conscious propaganda. There were so many firsts at the Hopkins, and they were news—not only to and for the medical profession but for the people, the sick who in those days were still being doctored chiefly by the horse-and-buggy doctors. These men were good and untiring, but they knew little of what was going on back East. When Osler, Kelly, Young, Cushing began crashing through with their brilliant exploits, when Finney began interpreting the better surgery, and Barker, Osler's successor, began talking and writing so lucidly, when rich man, poor man, beggar man, thief began to learn by devious routes, some of them of the grapevine variety, they started by-passing their local doctors for the trek to Baltimore. And I know that too, because I saw it.

To give you one example, I knew a man who came to Baltimore, had Dr. Osler go over him once in his office, and went away cured. No hospitalization. No exhaustive study. No medicines. He had had for years an intractable diarrhea following typhoid fever. Doctors in America and Europe had made tests and more tests. He had taken medicines and cures—one of them in Karlsbad, where great German doctors had assured him of the cure that did not materialize. Yet one consultation with Osler—cost $25—did the trick. The magic name, the magic word. "It's all nervous with you," said the great clinician. "Go your way; forget about yourself; stop taking medicines; stop taking cures; stay away from doctors."

Can you imagine a more dramatic thing than that man's recovery—which, by the way, was permanent? Can you imagine a more voluble, enthusiastic, unsolicited agent? And when later on in life that same man returned and had his prostate successfully removed by Hugh Young he all but took the stump for the Hopkins.

Yes, the Hopkins became the Supreme Court, and the only place in the United States I ever thought touched it was and still is the Mayo Clinic. There, too, did the magic word arise; there, too, did new and unusual feats press forward until they crashed the headlines and gave rise to the same kind of trek that was making its way to the Hopkins—big rich, the poor, the lame, the halt, the blind, often by-passing doctors as well as hospitals. A product of the Middle West, I saw something of that, too—firsthand.

It is all the more interesting and revealing because the Mayo Clinic and the Hopkins are so dissimilar—yet so alike. They are Americana in the highest sense, in that they started from nothing and made huge successes. Men built them, and they built men— while accomplishing the high purpose of curing the sick, carrying out investigative work of importance, spreading the gospel of the healing art to all who would listen and learn. Curiously enough, they were born at almost the same time in the last century but in different parts of the country and from different beginnings.

Indeed, in their method of origin they were as far apart as the poles. The Eastern institution was a rich man's dream come true. Everything money could buy, even including brains, was there, and the measure of success lay only in the ability and driving force to carry out preconceived plans. The other, that of the Middle West, was a poor man's work—not his dream, certainly not at the beginning. William W. Mayo was a practicing physician in a rural area and fought his own way through vicissitudes that would have stopped a man of less courage and fortitude.

His two sons, William C. and Charles, began to help him the moment they became doctors, or shortly thereafter, and driven on by the same force, the same spirit that gave their father no rest, they built up from extremely humble beginnings the superb institution that now bears their name. No master plan there. No early masterminding. No Welch, no Osler, Halsted, or Kelly. No great name at all. Nothing but sheer unadulterated American self-confidence and courage coupled with native ability. The masterminding came later and it was of high quality.

So from the two ends of the earth, as it were, the Hopkins and the Mayo Clinic have approached each other in that they are outstanding American institutions in their respective spheres; they are the two American institutions with the magic name. The one, part and parcel of an endowed university, the other a self-contained unit built up with private funds and operated as a private corporation for profit and self-perpetuation. If you wonder how two such dissimilar institutions could have risen to preeminence simultaneously and in such short period of time, if you ask how it happened that they could have wielded so much influence on the medicine of our day—and probably that of tomorrow—the answer must be that this is America.

Chapter 21

HOPKINS POLICY WITH REGARD TO ITS CLINICAL MEN. FIVE SITTING DUCKS AND A SECONDARY MEDICAL CENTER

IT IS SOMETIMES possible to see things in retrospect that, lightly regarded or even escaping notice at the time of their occurrence, had significant effect—even to changing the whole course of events. I think we can view in this light the failure of Hopkins authorities to liberalize their policy toward their own clinicians—from 1900 until some years after America's participation in World War I in 1917—by which time it was too late to change. The policy resulted in the development too early of a virile group of competing hospitals out in the city of Baltimore—in effect a "Secondary Medical Center," separate and distinct from the Hopkins, yet dominated chiefly by its own sons. It was to cost the Hopkins heavily in many ways, not the least of which was in men. In the opinion of some it was to be the reason for a certain loss of preeminence, once age and the normal wear and tear of life began to take toll of its early stalwarts—from 1922 on. The institution had lost too many men who might have aided in renewing the failing fire.

A singular lack of imagination seems to have been displayed. Following the early exciting success of the Hopkins it was a foregone conclusion that many of its own graduates would remain in Baltimore. They would go into practice; they would seek and probably obtain minor privileges of one sort or another at the Hopkins —work in the dispensaries and laboratories. With the Hospital and Medical school expanding there was room for them and even demand. Older, more experienced men, busy with teaching and work in the hospital wards and private pavilions, couldn't be expected to do the hundred and one little things attendant on a vigorous and growing institution. The younger graduates hanging around filled a need and found their niche. Some of them had completed residencies of several years at the Hopkins and elsewhere, others had

142

had but the one year's internship. They were young, eager and
well trained, but, in the nature of things, not distinguished. Whether
any of them ever would be distinguished lay in the laps of the gods.

In addition to these men there were certain other ones—not Hopkins graduates—who, having been attracted to the institution, had
become residents, or, like John M. T. Finney, had been taken on
after residency elsewhere. They went out into the city to practice
first. Being somewhat older and more experienced, also perhaps
more mature, they led the way and gained early prestige, but the
graduates did uncommonly well, and altogether it wasn't too long
before the names of Finney, Cullen, Bloodgood, Russell, Frank R.
Smith, L. P. Hamburger,* Tom Brown, Hunner, Richardson, Austrian, Fisher, Baer, Wolman, Pancoast, Earl Moore, Walter Baetjer,
Slack, Stone and others became almost household words in Baltimore.
Even Cushing went into practice, and also Thayer, Futcher, Boggs,
Hamman, these latter being medical consultants. They all had teaching positions at the Hopkins but were paid little or nothing, and it
was either practice or starve. They chose not to starve.

It was at this juncture that the Hopkins masterminds might have
used more imagination. They should have seen that the private
wards at Hopkins were entirely inadequate and unless they were
expanded it would be impossible to hold desirable men. They should
have seen that they themselves had forced the issue by not paying
men of the lower echelons adequate salaries. For once the good old
custom of hospital authorities exploiting doctors backfired in no
uncertain manner. The Hopkins couldn't possibly do without these
men, yet because of the small number of beds on the private wards,
it compelled them either to go out and find other hospitals wherein
they could do their private work, or stay out of business. They
found the other hospitals, and from that day forward were in a
position literally to thumb their noses at the Hopkins.

You might say that hindsight is better than foresight and that it
was too much to ask of the Hopkins directorate to see so far and so
clearly into the future. Or you might say that it wasn't a case of

---

* Oldest living graduate.

using imagination at all, the Hopkins directorate had a policy and stuck to it. This policy did not include office buildings for staff men in private practice, large private wards, and still larger free wards. Which was all well and good, or would have been if it had worked. It didn't work, and some of the most promising men the Hopkins possessed forthwith began building up other institutions. One could slyly suggest that that was the cue for the directors of the University of Maryland to step in and grab them. They didn't; but what a gesture that would have been!

It is of interest that the men chiefly affected were the surgeons, who needed a place in which to operate. With medicine still in its swaddling clothes physicians could handle their patients in the home, and most of them were doing it. Of even greater interest were five Baltimore institutions waiting like "sitting ducks" to be plucked—small borderline medical places mostly of the sectarian aged-home type. Situated as they were in different sections, they formed a sort of enveloping or protective ring around the city and were the answer to the surgeon's prayer.

John M. T. Finney was the first to take notice and he had the old Union Protestant Infirmary—not far from the main residential district—well on its way to being a real hospital before the community realized what was taking place. Thomas Cullen and associates took over the Church Home and Infirmary—only five blocks away from the Hopkins Hospital—and that, too, promptly lost much of its Old Home character. Third to be plucked was the St. Agnes Hospital, way out on the western fringe of Baltimore. Its situation had militated against its broad usefulness until the dynamic Joseph C. Bloodgood took hold, and then the location somehow didn't seem to matter so much. The remaining two institutions, Hospital for the Women of Maryland and the Hebrew Aged Home did not come under the sway of any one man in particular but eventually fell to distinctive groups from the Hopkins. I should say that men from the University of Maryland were included in all five places in minor capacities but they hadn't taken over and transformed them because necessity had not driven them as it had the man from the

Hopkins. They had adequate facilities at the University of Maryland, and such outside needs as came up were found in several other going hospitals of long history. St. Joseph's was one, and Mercy Hospital was another.

In none of the above institutions was anything of the strong-arm invasive method involved in getting control, nor were the aged and infirm put out. On the contrary, they were given care and consideration by the newcomers and, if anything, were better off than before. The only difference was that such rooms and quarters as they didn't require were turned over for more definite hospital purposes. It was a slow, gradual process, with the authorities of each institution realizing that a great opportunity was presented for broader usefulness. No one attempted to take control or supervision away from them; rather, the original groups in control were encouraged to remain and carry on. It was the smartest thing the Hopkins men ever did. At one fell swoop they made lasting friends, got the utmost in cooperation and understanding—and, of course, money. The original controlling authorities were highly regarded representatives of their respective groups, and had enormous potentialities for opening certain of Baltimore's bulging purses. All they needed was the know-how, and that the newly admitted doctors pleasantly supplied.

The rest is history, even though the Hopkins and the city of Baltimore have not to this day grasped its broad significance or reviewed it in true perspective. In course of time all five institutions had their faces lifted and their bodies enlarged by grafts of new buildings, operating rooms, and laboratories. They became large hospitals of quality, and two of them changed their names. One moved to a better location, and another is contemplating it. These five hospitals now constitute the backbone of Baltimore's very excellent hospital system and are, in effect, the city's Secondary Medical Center. Above all, they became the training ground for large numbers of young Hopkins graduates who would otherwise have been blacked out by the parent institution's continued rigid adherence to the policy that had threatened Finney, Cullen, and Bloodgood—to say nothing of a host of other lesser lights.

I think it was this latter event—the training of younger men outside its own precincts—that eventually backfired so effectively against the Hopkins. But in explaining it I find myself in the predicament of saying something that will probably rouse a storm of protest. In its earlier days, disregarding the "Four Saints," the strongest and most dynamic men at the Hopkins, the men who went out and did things, were the surgeons and gynecologists. At least they were more in the public eye. In part this was due to the fact that medicine had not reached the buoyant scientific heights of today, while surgery was well on its way, but in greater measure it was because of the men themselves. They were producing spectacularly; they were telling the world; and the world was listening and applauding. If, as I say, you leave Welch, Osler, Halsted, and Kelly out of the picture, it was the surgeons, chiefly, who were putting the Hopkins on the map.

Yet, with the exception of Cushing and Hugh Young, the Hopkins brass hats could not see them. They appeared to regard them more in the light of practical wielders of the knife who were out to make big money and had little interest in scientific values and laboratory work. Even the eminent Dr. Kelly found it "more congenial" to establish a private hospital and do most of his work there, and I have no doubt that if Hugh Young hadn't corralled Diamond Jim Brady and shaken him down for a clinic of his own, he, too, would have been given "the gate" in so far as hospital beds were concerned.

I am telling the story as I saw and understood it, a story in which I played a minor role. We of a younger generation often skirted this subject in our many intimate discussions but as I recall we never quite understood it. I suppose we were too close up and perhaps too immature to understand basic matters. We couldn't correlate things, either, and were unable to think the strange happenings through—as I am trying to do now—and cause and effect were lost on us. Our personal woes probably weighed too heavily and each man saw things chiefly as they affected him. Little did we dream that the time would come when we would have high rank at the Hopkins—with big practices on the outside—and that certain ones of us would have much to do with shaping its course—even that of American medicine.

Those were the days when well-trained, eager young men at the Hopkins sat around bemoaning the fate that seemed to thwart their every ambition. The ring of hospitals I'm talking about was only in process of developing into the superior Secondary Medical Center it was to become, and no one, Hopkins men or others, quite appreciated the turn of events then shaping up—or indeed the impact of tomorrow's medicine in its broadest sense. Even at this late date I do not believe the movement that took place in Baltimore at that time with regard to men and hospitals in relation to the Johns Hopkins and medicine generally has had the consideration and study it merits. Not once have I heard the rise of the five hospitals mentioned in the light of a definite movement brought about by necessity. People and doctors have noted each hospital's separate course without grasping the essential fact of their harmonious, if unconscious, unity. I confess to not having seen it myself until I set myself to the task of telling the Hopkins story, when it suddenly dawned on me in its true light. The Hopkins masterminds had a blind spot and acted as if they didn't want it lifted. In effect they said to their graduates, "Yes, you may work in the hospital's dispensaries and help teach but you can expect no remuneration or ward privileges—either free or private." So the boys played the game and went to work and for the time being felt amply repaid by the pleasant associations, the huge clinical opportunities, and the experience in teaching they were receiving.

To queries the masterminds said, "If any of you wish to indulge in research the laboratories are at your disposal, but you do not have to do work of this sort, and we make no promises of any kind in the way of promotion to staff positions." Nobody said anything about what would happen if a man came through with something worth while because that was problematical at best, and the young surgeons for the most part had had little or no special scientific or laboratory training. Cushing had, of course. He was in charge of the Hunterian Laboratory and he was the most erudite of men with a background of the broadest training. The only other man like him or even approaching his mental stature was the Professor himself—Halsted, who was more the philosopher than Cushing.

It so happened, though, that certain of the young surgeons, whether inspired by the Professor or Cushing or through chance or sheer cussedness, did produce. Not only did they produce, but they did it along needed lines and at the psychological moment. You might say that the plastic surgery and blood transfusion and intestinal obstruction work they did in the Hunterian was not entirely and absolutely downright original—in that nobody had ever before thought along those lines or done anything in them—but the work and the results obtained were in advance of anything hitherto accomplished, nothing of the sort was being done elsewhere in Baltimore, at the Hopkins Hospital or any other place, and it looked good.

Yet when the time came for transfer from the laboratory to the clinic, when the work had progressed to the point where human beings who needed the relief these things offered should be given the privilege of accepting or rejecting them, the brass hats again spoke.

"No, my sons," they said—again in effect, of course; in reality nothing was said; it just was understood that men not of the inner circles did not rate—"it is against our policy to give you the privileges of our free wards wherein to try these interesting and perhaps useful things. Our free ward beds are limited and are only sufficient for the activities of upper level staff members and our residents. If you were, perchance, residents or upper level staff men you could make trial; but you are not and so must go elsewhere."

There was no "elsewhere." The young men in question had no privileges in any hospital at that time and they had few patients—free or private. Not then, in the years around 1908–1909–1910 and thereabouts. Later on they did—plenty. So they kept on working in the laboratory and making progress, and sick people in the Hopkins Hospital right across the street, who needed badly the succor they could give, kept on needing it—and not getting it. If you ask why the resident at the Hopkins and upper level staff men didn't try out the things these young men developed in the laboratories, the answer is that that is "not cricket." In the first place, the man who makes a discovery, perfects a device, makes an advance in the field of medicine, is supposed to have the right to make the first clinical trial (for better or worse); and, in the second place, the other fellow wouldn't know how unless he were specially taught —and, naturally, the "boys" wouldn't be that generous. There was a third reason which I dislike mentioning because it is embarrassing. The older men of the day at the Hopkins did not entirely appreciate the broad significance and the timeliness of all the work in question. If I am going to tell of happenings, I am compelled to set down my honest convictions.

However, the *status quo* did not last too long. Dr. J. M. T. Finney got wind of it and being more practical-minded, less dogmatic— possibly also more social-minded—promptly offered all the facilities he possessed in his own clinic at the Union Protestant Infirmary, and in short order Bloodgood and Cullen did likewise at theirs. That, too, is history, and history that has been talked about plenty "in the lodge" but not hitherto made public. Under the most careful and painstaking supervision the products of laboratory experimentation done at the Hopkins were given clinical trial at these other institutions—and proved their worth. From that time on there was presented the strange spectacle of surgeons graduating at the Hopkins, teaching at the Hopkins, working in its laboratories, writing books and treatises based on that work, being permitted to operate in every hospital in the city *but* the Hopkins. All the men were given recognition at the Hopkins in the form of staff rank but not so-called "privileges." Few people—doctors or laymen—knew this. Only with their intimates did the men chiefly affected discuss it. As of that day children were seen and not heard, and youth was anything but rampant. The heavy hand was always in evidence.

I think you can see what a fortunate circumstance it was that the fringe hospitals had been taken over. By the time the above-mentioned "impasse" began to crack, roughly around 1910, four of them—the Hebrew Aged Home developed later—were well on their way to becoming completely integrated hospitals with house staffs, nurses' training schools, and all. They had medical services, children's wards, wards for female surgery, wards for general surgery, X rays, laboratories, and even small dispensaries. None of them were teaching hospitals in the sense that medical students were in attendance or formal clinics were given, but there was plenty of the highest grade instruction for younger staff men and visiting doctors. These latter increased day by day because of the wide reputations Finney, Cullen, and Bloodgood had made before they took on their new activities. Once it became known that they had their own clinics and were in a position to give bigger and better demonstrations in them than they had been permitted to give at the Hopkins, their admirers promptly changed over and followed them. (You understand that Cullen, Finney, Bloodgood, and their associates maintained their connection with the Hopkins at all times. They just didn't do the bulk of their work there for the reasons mentioned.)

I think it can be said, however, that no small part of the startling success of the Union Protestant Infirmary, the Church Home and Infirmary, St. Agnes Hospital, and the Hospital for the Women of Maryland was due to their wise policy of opening their doors to young doctors. As the years progressed, more advanced work in more fields than one was being done in them than in the Hopkins itself. What more natural than that doctors from the "provinces" learned about it and forthwith began flooding their patients in more than ever. They came to see and sit at the feet of the three masters—Finney, Cullen, and Bloodgood—and were not disappointed. While doing that they came in contact with the young doctors and were impressed. Be it said to their credit, the Big Three never attempted to keep their young men in the background.

That, in brief, is the story of the development of Baltimore's Secondary Medical Center. There was a spirit to it and good fellowship, but different from that at the Hopkins. Young men, both physicians and surgeons, were given opportunities without regard to any consideration other than ability and playing the game. Wards as well as semiprivate and private room facilities were thrown open to them. The highest possible moral and professional tone prevailed, and men not imbued with it were never entirely comfortable and soon departed of their own volition. Altogether, it was a strangely satisfying relationship that existed among these four hospitals which, separately run and not entirely pointing to the same things in medicine, nevertheless maintained a sort of unwritten association. To a considerable extent their staffs were interlocking. In all the forty years I have been connected with them I have never once known any one of them to have a serious fuss or internal disagreement, professional or otherwise. And if you don't think that is a record, just look about you and consult the annals of hospitals and doctor groups in your own and other communities.

Looked at with the cold eye of objectivity the Hopkins attitude was more a case of bad judgment than anything else—coupled with a surprising lack of elasticity, both mental and practical. The Hopkins simply missed the boat. In the late John Staige Davis it had America's foremost pioneer in plastic surgery. If it had played its cards wisely, it would have today the greatest clinic in the world in that much-needed and growing branch of endeavor. It would also have the great clinic for peripheral vascular diseases it should long since have had. Because of Dr. Halsted's outstanding work in this field and that of his many assistants, the Hopkins was the leader of them all, yet it never even made a gesture toward capitalizing on these riches. Other prominent institutions have seen fit to do that on very much less wealth, and as time passes and the importance of studying and dealing with vascular affections becomes clearer, more are doing it. But not the Hopkins. The Hopkins, erstwhile pioneer, sits back and sulks, and the parade passes it by. Nor can it be truthfully said that long years ago the need for such a clinic with its vast inherent possibilities was not repeatedly agitated. To those who would say that the Hopkins did not want clinics of the type mentioned—preferring to develop others like the Departments of Psychiatry, Eye, Hygiene, Institute for the History of Medicine, etc.—I would ask why not. Why not have both types?

These matters are part and parcel of the Hopkins story, and I see no reason for passing them by. It was exactly the same as if the General Motors Corporation had had its young men develop a fine car with all sorts of gadgets and then when they went out and advertised it and got a lot of orders, refused to produce it in quantity. Whereupon the men, in desperation, transferred their orders to

Chrysler and Studebaker, who were only too glad to fill them. Nor was that all. In a sense a false impression was being created which resulted in no little embarrassment to the men. The talks they made before medical societies, the papers and books they wrote all carried their Hopkins Medical School and Hospital ranks under their names.* What more natural than that doctors and patients alike not in the know thought their clinical work was being done at the Hopkins and forthwith gravitated there? Only when they reached Baltimore or, as sometimes happened, were actually admitted to the Hopkins was it discovered that the men in question hadn't privileges. Just how many patients there have been over the years who ostensibly came to the Hopkins and never even saw it no one knows, but they must have been legion, and the trek still goes on. How much this has cost the Hopkins in prestige—also in dollars and cents— is any man's guess.

The system, of course, was responsible—not any one man or group of men. The Hopkins was a "closed" institution; that is, an institution chiefly for research and teaching and with a staff organized and adequate for those purposes only. It would appear that no thought was given to possible expansion and the larger staff that would be required—more particularly to the impact of young men pressing for a place in the sun. Those doctors at the helm of the Hopkins in its early years were naïve and unworldly. Other than in matters of science they were totally unable to project their minds into the world of tomorrow—if, indeed, it ever occurred to them to do it.

Not until long years later—after World War I, in fact, by which time expansion had gotten under way and most of the original doctors-in-charge had passed on—was the error noted and steps taken to correct it. Unfortunately, the gesture then made was too little and too late. A whole generation of men who would have loved nothing better than to remain closely associated with their alma mater had assumed other obligations, and with them loyalties that could not morally be denied.

* Later on, some of the men omitted these.

Chapter 22

JOHN M. T. FINNEY. HALSTED AND FINNEY

It was strange indeed the way John M. T. Finney was handled by the Hopkins. For years on end they just couldn't see him, or saw him only in the guise of "another operating surgeon," of more than usual ability, perhaps, but not outstanding. They missed utterly the man, his broad humanity, his understanding of people—well and sick—his astonishing ability to teach and to make friends. He actually became the foremost surgeon of America, first citizen of Baltimore and Maryland, surgeon to and friend of Presidents, financiers, priests, and preachers, the little man as well as the big man—and finally the representative of the Hopkins before doctors, more especially surgeons. Dr. Halsted, aloof, retiring, couldn't bring himself to meet people or doctors. He rarely attended medical meetings; never, so far as I know, headed societies. He was the brooding philosopher pure and simple, and the investigator.

So Finney became the man of Hopkins that doctors elsewhere looked to. Finney who was next to Halsted in rank and who taught third-year students—only in the dispensary, be it said; rarely in the wards—and gave one operative clinic a week, but whose chief activities were at the Union Protestant Infirmary, a little, inadequate place of hardly 150 beds that he and his friends later expanded into the beautiful 400-bed Union Memorial Hospital. That was where he gave the brilliant operative clinics that attracted doctors in droves and that was where he took his countless private patients— rich and poor alike. All because they failed to take his measure at the Hopkins. Some men held it against him that he personally did no research work, and it was true. He did not personally work in laboratories. He often remarked that some men didn't have the urge, and he was one of them. But he made up for his own lack by encouraging those who did, and not only that, he gave them clinical opportunities when those who should have done so refused. He did even more. He actually gave struggling young physicians and surgeons private patients so that they could make enough money to

153

live. Always, of course, with the patient's consent. He would simply explain to patients that a certain young man of his acquaintance—associated with him, he'd sometimes say—had done special work and could really do a better job on them than he could. He would stand by or, in certain cases, assist, but it was understood that the budding youngster would make whatever charge was agreed upon—Finney himself making none.

It would be idle to give a list of honors that were showered upon Dr. Finney, but two might be mentioned. Princeton University sought him as President, after Woodrow Wilson left in 1910 to be Governor of New Jersey and later President of the United States. Loyal alumnus and long a trustee, Dr. Finney thought long and hard before refusing his alma mater's call, and his mental anguish was plain to be seen. Enormous pressure was exerted on him, and the University's need was great, but refuse he did, and those who knew him best thought it was his innate love for medicine—which he would necessarily have had to relinquish—coupled with the obligation he felt he owed to the many young doctors dependent on him.

The second great honor was that of first President of the American College of Surgeons in 1913. I know for a fact that Dr. Finney did not want this position. He realized that it would take loads of time and energy to whip the society into shape—with endless conferences and meetings away from his work. He knew, too, that great firmness would be required if high standards were to be maintained and he foresaw much unpleasantness. Since the idea for the College hadn't originated with him or his close friends, he felt that others should take the helm. There were many such, and he pointed them out to Dr. Franklin Martin of Chicago, who visited him and urged him to start the thing off. The College was Martin's brain child, and he was a very determined man. Also a brainy one and cool, calculating, pleasantly persuasive to boot. If this society, modeled after the famed British College of Surgeons and intended to be the premier organization of surgeons in America, was ever to amount to much, it had to be properly launched. That meant that the President, above all, had to be a man of impeccable character, a leader professionally and socially, known to doctors and laymen alike for high accomplishments, farseeing and wise. There was no other surgeon in the United States who met these qualifications so well as Finney, and Martin and his cohorts brought so much pressure to bear that in the end they had their way. John M. T. Finney was inaugurated midst great acclaim at the first convocation in Chicago. He remained President three years—just long enough to see the society well on its way—after which he insisted on being excused. The present high place held by America's College of Surgeons is due in no small part to the influence and guidance of its first President.

If Finney had been a more aggressive character and Halsted a vindictive man, one or the other of them would have had to get out. The Hopkins would not have been big enough for them both. They were so unlike in every possible way that it would be a waste of time to make comparison. Yet withal they got along extremely well. There were some who thought the Professor was jealous of Finney's success in private practice and his growing popularity among doctors. They said that was the reason Finney was held back and hadn't more duties and influence at the Hopkins. Pure speculation and not warranted, so far as I was ever able to ascertain. Halsted was well fixed financially; he hadn't a family; he didn't like private practice and didn't care to be bothered; above all, he shunned social and professional contact except in rare and limited doses.

The reason he failed to delegate more duties to his first assistant was because his first assistant bore the rank in name only, and so did his second and third—and every other man on his staff except his chief resident. I have already touched upon the development of the resident system at the Hopkins and will only say here that Halsted was its stanch advocate. His resident became almost like a son to him, and if any group could be said really to know him, it was the several chief residents he had, and I say several advisedly because there weren't many. Although they always chose to remain closemouthed about him, one could sort of sense it in the little things. And were they superior! So each in his respective turn was

Halsted's first assistant. He was the man Halsted leaned on and delegated authority to, whether he was at home or on his various trips to Europe—not Finney, not Bloodgood, not Cushing (after his residency), or anybody else—and no man ever thought of questioning the resident or giving unsought advice. In this instance— the case of Finney—I would say that the Hopkins resident system backfired and did great harm, but more to the Hopkins than to Finney, who took it in good part. He was, I think, the most forgiving and forbearing of men—too much so, many of his friends thought. There was, for example, the opportunity he once had to retaliate on a particularly bad actor—a Hopkins ex-resident—but didn't. It happened in France, during World War I, after Finney became a big shot, and the doctor in question was in danger of being sent home. A man of ability, because of his tactics he had become *persona non grata* with the higher-ups, and they relieved him of his command. Swallowing his pride, he appealed to Dr. Finney and was saved. Those in the know wondered but were not entirely surprised. All Dr. Finney would say was, "He feels puny enough."

If there was one word in the English language that John M. T. Finney loved more than all others, it was "puny." It is expressive, isn't it?

But it was strange and certainly it was interesting to see Halsted and Finney together. Sometimes it was downright amusing. I don't think they liked each other, but there was mutual admiration and respect, the one for scientific attainments, the other for practical accomplishments. They never seemed comfortable or at ease in each other's presence and were never together for long. You didn't see them with their heads together laughing and joking and swapping stories like other men—this despite the fact that Finney was a born raconteur, and Halsted himself (at the rare dinner) could be witty and extremely humorous. They'd bow and scrape and be polite and stilted, with neither saying exactly what was in his mind, and then they'd part, and you'd almost hear the sigh of relief each gave as he went on his way. Yet when one time Mrs. Halsted needed to be operated on it was Finney who got the call. She recovered.

Halsted really was a character—and lovable when you got close to him, as I did upon rare occasions. The following story has nothing to do with Dr. Finney but is incorporated to show how Halsted could act. It concerned the final written examination at the end of my fourth year, and there were only three questions. Two were the usual kind, but the third concerned the lowly toothache.

"What would you do about toothache?" it said; and there you were. The eminent Professor hadn't said one word about teeth the whole year through, and nobody else had. In fact, you could go through the Hopkins then, and you can come pretty close to doing it now, without knowing that there are such things as teeth. Oh, they mention them occasionally and tell you to look at them and once in a while you see an X ray. Some fellow might even dilate on the trouble that comes from them—including their nuisance value—but as for any real downright dental instruction there is mighty little. There will be, of course, but they haven't gotten around to it, and only a few years back one student told me quite seriously that the best thing he knew to do about them was to "pull 'em—all." Maybe he's right, at that.

Well, anyhow, there we were in Dr. Halsted's examination with toothache before us and we all sort of "went to town" on it. I wrote volumes—chiefly because I couldn't write volumes on the others, as they were of the more abstruse Halstedian variety. Everyone was grinning when the ordeal was over, and there was much comparing of notes. No one knew whether his views were correct and no one ever found out whether the Professor liked what he got or not—that is, no one but myself. I asked him—not at the time, of course, but several years later when I came to know him better through some laboratory work he and I had a mutual interest in.

"Dr. Halsted," I said, "do you perchance recall the time you asked about toothache in a fourth-year final examination?"

"Why, yes, of course."

"Well, that was my class, and it was so unusual that I've often wondered what you were getting at."

He smiled, and in that gentle, soothing voice of his said, "I wasn't getting at anything specially. It just happened that I had been having a very bad time with one of my molars and, not being overly fond of dentists, it occurred to me to get some original ideas." Then he added, "I was extremely successful."

The truth of the matter was that Halsted and Finney complemented each other though they didn't realize it. Doctors came and listened to the Professor, and most of them went away shaking their heads. They came and watched him operate and were much impressed with the meticulous manner in which he performed but felt that he wasted time on little things and that was the reason it took him so long. They didn't understand, of course, and it was Finney over at the Union Protestant Infirmary who interpreted Halsted's methods and put things in practical form so that Mr. Average Surgeon could understand and do them.

Not every man had the patience to transfix and tie every minute blood vessel in a thyroid or breast operation as Halsted did; and, truth to tell, it wasn't absolutely necessary. But Halsted was always aiming at perfection and was interested more in the theoretical than the practical, the individual rather than the many. It has to be that way with the pioneer. Yet the many have to be considered, and desirable as perfection is, you can usually do with less. You have to in mass production, and in the present instance it was Finney who showed the way. Where Halsted took four hours to do a cancer of the breast—and skin-grafted every case—Finney knew that that would never do for practical purposes and, using Halsted's main ideas, showed how much the same thing could be accomplished with no skin-grafting and in one-third the time. Other surgeons contributed, too, and though their percentages of cures never were quite as high as Halsted's they were nearly so, and considering the greatest good to the greatest number their results were entirely satisfactory.

But Finney was by no means always the follower or interpreter. He had ideas of his own and put them to practical use, without benefit of laboratory. His pyloroplasty for ulcer of the stomach— he gave much credit for it to his associate Omar Pancoast—received world-wide recognition; and the present-day subtotal thyroidectomy for toxic goiter was his conception, even though he was not the first to publish it. Like the honest, careful man he was, he felt that the number of cases he had done was not sufficient to justify definite conclusions, and though urged to make a preliminary note he refused—and so lost priority. Others who came and saw, or maybe just had the same idea, beat him to it, but I can't say that it ever bothered him. Nothing of that sort gave him the slightest concern.

With all his qualities and abilities and constructive works, though, this many-sided man was not an executive. And that's a funny thing, because he really did things and at times had great authority and tremendous responsibility. His method was that of lots of big-minded men. He always had with him a trusted associate who had the executive ability and other qualities he lacked—understanding of finance was one—and it was he who actually did these things. Finney had an uncanny way of sizing up men; getting just the right fellow for the job and then letting him have his head. If there was an occasional glaring mistake, the reason was usually to be found in his heart. Down-and-outers and the weak always made appeal to him, and every once in a while he had reason to regret an action. But it wasn't often.

No, my friends, I was not Dr. Finney's good right arm. That fortunate individual was Dr. William A. Fisher, Hopkins graduate, noted surgeon in his own right, diplomat, executive and self-effacing adviser, all rolled into one. Throughout life Dr. Finney leaned on Fisher and never once found him wanting. Wherever you saw Finney you had only to look and somewhere in the offing would be Fisher. If it was running a hospital or building one, if it was seeing a patient or doing an operation Dr. Finney didn't have time for or couldn't do for other reasons, there was always Fisher. Even when it came to the war and service in France, there, too, was the same trusted aide who ringmastered things. Stout fella, Fisher. Hundreds of doctors will agree to that.

I was just one of those Dr. Finney taught and liked a little and permitted to help him upon occasion. I had a hand in some of his literary work, and in the early days I did all his blood transfusions.

In fact, he gave me my first chance to use the apparatus for this work which I had devised in the Hunterian Laboratory at the Hopkins, and that was the beginning of a lifelong friendship.

Finney was not a dynamic man, but somehow or other he always seemed to take his objective once he decided it was worth while. Essentially he was a man of peace and compromise but he had strong convictions and he did his own thinking. Moreover, he was fearless. This was never better illustrated than when he wrote the foreword to my book, *Medicine at the Crossroads*, published in 1939. He told me frankly that he did not subscribe to most of the things I was advocating but thought people and doctors alike ought to read of them and decide for themselves.

"Times are changing," he said, "and medicine is, too. You could be right."

So he wrote what he thought was the proper thing and then I got worried. Dr. Finney is getting on in years, I said to myself, and he has always had a high place in medicine—more particularly entrenched medicine. What will his friends say if he comes out now sponsoring a book that takes the newer, different social approach, and suppose he is made unhappy by criticism, however undeserved and unjust? I would never forgive myself if that were to happen.

So I took the foreword back to him and told him what was in my mind. We always had a close, cordial relationship, and I felt sure he'd see my point, but he didn't. On the contrary, he was a little annoyed. I had asked him if he had consulted any of his other friends or his sons before agreeing to write the foreword.

"No," he snapped. "Why should I?"

"Well—uh—that is, Dr. Finney," I began to stammer, "they might take a different viewpoint and—uh—sort of suggest that maybe it would be wiser for you not to do so."

"Humph!"

"And now that I think it over, maybe they'd be right."

"Now listen and get this straight," he said. "I'm old enough to decide matters for myself and I don't need advice from anyone. The views expressed in this book don't especially appeal to me, but you've gone out and got experience different from most men at the Hopkins. I advised you to do it. You ought to know what you are talking about, and people ought to read it. Let's not have any more talk about the matter."

The foreword appeared, and there were no repercussions, but I wasn't the only one who was nervous.

Men of the John M. T. Finney type are, fortunately, not so rare in America. You see them in different walks of life and in different parts of the country, and always the pattern is the same. They are simple, God-fearing, tolerant men who have ability and broad humanity and they are the bulwark of our nation. To know them well, to be close to them is to be blessed. Friends love to tell stories about them, and there usually are many that they can tell—and true ones. That is part of their charm and their humanity, the fact that there is so much to tell.

One of mine about Dr. Finney—and only one, for I could tell many—concerns the time, rather late in his life, when the great man fell ill. He had what we surgeons call "a gall bladder," and the boys finally got him to give up and come into the Hospital as a patient. He'd fought it off—doctorlike—as long as he could and there he was at last, disgusted with himself and the world in general. Under ordinary circumstances he'd have been operated on promptly, and that would have been the end of it, but since he was so important his doctors elected to wait and back and fill until —well—you know. It's always the same.

They didn't want him to have many visitors, and that was wise, because everybody in Baltimore wanted to come to see him. So we all dutifully stayed away until one day in midafternoon I chanced to be walking down the hall—purely by accident, of course!—and, seeing the door to his room half open, I sort of wandered in. His nurse was out. He was lying on his side with the most woebegone expression on his face, and though he didn't look especially ill you could see that he was unhappy.

He gave me a wry smile as I took his outstretched hand, and in the most long-suffering voice said, "Bernie, do you know a good doctor?"

"No, sir," I replied. "I honestly don't. The only doctor I ever had any confidence in is myself and sometimes I kinda—"

He grinned and didn't let me finish.

"Well, that's just the way it is with me right now," he said, half sitting up, and his voice beginning to take on some of its usual vibrant quality. "If these fellows around here would just let me handle this case, we'd get somewhere, but did you ever try to argue with your own doctor?"

It was so funny I burst out laughing, and he did, too, though he had to hold his side because of the stitch. That was the one thing he'd always preached against—doctors trying to treat themselves when sick.

But at that the boys pulled a boner with him. They decided to let him go home for a spell and wait for a more propitious time for operation, and while he was waiting—or before, for all anyone knows—his gall bladder ruptured. Providence was on his side, though, and things were so walled off by adhesions that no damage resulted, and the operation, which was finally done, went off satisfactorily. Bill Fisher did it, of course, and it was then that the group did a real smart thing, perhaps the only one during the whole episode. They didn't permit anyone in the operating room but those actually concerned with the operation. They were afraid of too much advice—and correctly so. I guess they thought maybe they'd had too much already.

Some months later Dr. Finney confided to me that he had taught us all wrong about gall bladders. "When you first see a patient in an attack you should give him a *half grain* of morphine right off the bat and repeat it if the pain isn't relieved within a very few minutes. None of this piddling business of a quarter grain and waiting before repeating like I've been advising."

"Which means, sir," I replied, "that it all depends on whose ox is gored after all, doesn't it?"

He walked away laughing; he had always had a wonderful sense of humor.

John M. T. Finney was a humble man with an inspirational quality for all those with whom he came in contact. He was the most Christlike man I have ever known.

Chapter 23

HOPKINS JUMPS THE GUN ON FULL TIME.
WORLD WAR I

IT IS POSSIBLE to view America's participation (1917) in World War I as an opportune diversion for the Hopkins—the hand of fate, as it were, reaching out to stay it from going ahead with a badly timed, ill-considered movement of unknown imponderables.

Others may disagree with me, but to my mind there was no occasion for the Johns Hopkins or any other medical school putting the men of its clinical departments on "full time" in the early 1900's, and the reasons given were not convincing. Thirty-five years later— as of the present—we see a very different picture, and the demands of scientific medical advance alone are reasons more than sufficient for integrating the system—not only at the Hopkins but eventually and by degrees in all medical schools. Perhaps I should say that the term "full time" in medicine is used to denote complete devotion to teaching, research, and hospital work in the one institution that pays the salary. The doctors concerned have no other outside interests of private or free practice, business, or anything.

In the early 1900's medicine had hardly begun to come alive. We were just beginning to realize the far-reaching possibilities of bacteriology, X ray, physiological chemistry, biophysics, and all the other adjuncts that burst forth so importantly in later years. Doctors were still relying chiefly on their eyes, ears, hands, senses, and patients' histories for diagnosis—using laboratory methods in so far as they would go, which wasn't so far—and few indeed were the antitoxins, serums, and such available. There were no wonder drugs. To say, therefore, that professors of medicine, surgery, obstetrics, gynecology, and pediatrics should eschew private practice because it took too much of their time—time that could better be devoted to research and teaching—didn't make sense. The very reputation, the very prominence of the Hopkins proved the contrary. Osler, Halsted, Kelly, Cushing, Bloodgood, Cullen, Finney, Williams, Thayer, Barker, Futcher—all these and others who were making real contributions to medicine had their private practices. Yet they seemed to have all the time needed for hospital and teaching duties. They seemed also to have all the knowledge and experience required.

In short, the Hopkins "jumped the gun" on the question of full time and was only saved by the war. Not, however, before the very estimable and highly regarded Barker, successor to Osler, had resigned the Chair of Medicine in preference to going on full time, and no inconsiderable staff disaffection had arisen. For once in his life Dr. Welch, even though putting across to a limited degree his cherished idea, had not been convincing to the clinical men. He is reported to have informed the Rockefeller Foundation, which financed the deal, that the men were in agreement with him, but it was my impression that that was far from true. Then the war came along, and except for a very few key positions, things were held in abeyance—not only for the actual period of the war but for more than two decades thereafter, which is eloquent proof that the time for full time wasn't ripe, nor were the reasons given sound. The best that can be said, I think, is that Dr. Welch and his associates probably foresaw an eventuality—which in itself is an accomplishment—but misjudged the fundamentals as well as the timing. It is a pity that they could not have lived to see the newer medicine which was to bring their brainchild to actual and assured fruition—to be discussed in more detail in a later chapter.

World War I brought the Hopkins up sharp—as it did all medical institutions. The wheels of peace stopped in their tracks, and forthwith all medical energies were bent to the one purpose of aiding the sick and the wounded who were bound to come in overwhelming numbers. A hospital unit of 500 beds—some forty officers and seventy-five nurses—was organized and with Dr. John M. T. Finney, director, sailed with the first convoy of American troops sent to France.

I do not propose to give the detailed story of this organization, but it was unique in many ways, and certain high lights cannot be omitted. They very definitely comprise part of the greater Hopkins story. For example, the unit took over with it thirty-two medical students who were just entering the fourth-year class. They had volunteered and went as enlisted personnel. Throughout the winter and spring of 1917–1918 they were given such instruction as the staff had time for and per telegraphic orders were graduated just one year from the date of sailing—June, 1918. The government immediately commissioned them first lieutenants in the Medical Corps, and they were forthwith distributed to outfits that needed them. The whole business was most unorthodox—but hardly more so than many other American procedures. No group in the A.E.F. gave a better account of itself than these thirty-two men—both in the ranks and later as officers. Several were seriously wounded in battle.

A detail from the Hopkins Unit organized the first American army hospital in France. It was in St. Nazaire, the Port of Landing, and the Hopkins group ran it for over two months, at which time a hospital unit arrived from the States and took over. The experience in military matters thereby gained was of inestimable value in setting up the hospital in the troop-training area, Vosges Mountains, where the Hopkins was to have its base. This was in the little town of Bazoilles-sur-Meuse, and the unit officially became Base Hospital No. 18, A.E.F. Here the Hopkins had another first in that for long weeks it was the only hospital with the American troops pouring into the area for training. They had plenty of sick and wounded— the latter due chiefly to inexperience with the newer instruments of war.

It was a cold, bitter, discouraging winter, during the course of which American troops were thrown into the battle line (trenches) for the first time. The outfit was a comparatively small detachment of the 16th Infantry, and the sector was supposed to be a quiet one. And so it was until the Americans came up, whereupon all hell suddenly broke loose—and Base Hospital No. 18, A.E.F., got the men who were left. This was the first actual battle surgery the Hopkins men had ever done and it was ghastly. Fortunately, they had been sent to French and British fronts beforehand and had had some instruction in the famous "*débridement* operation" that was required. This consists of ruthlessly cutting away every vestige of devitalized tissue, only main blood vessels and nerves being spared. It was something to take. The experience proved to be only the preview of coming events.

From that time on events moved swiftly. Other units from America's great hospitals began coming in, great preparations were in the making, and very soon the Hopkins Unit found itself completely shorn of all its older, higher ranking medical officers—from Dr. Finney on down. They were needed by the Army's Medical Department to help run things. Dr. Finney became a brigadier general, Chief Consulting Surgeon of the A.E.F., and more than any other one man, in my estimation, was responsible for the excellence of America's surgical effort. His right-hand man was Dr. William A. Fisher, also from the Hopkins Unit. The younger doctors took over Base No. 18 and ran it throughout the duration. Underlings at the Hopkins, most of them more actively associated with Baltimore's secondary medical center, they went over as captains and lieutenants and all remained so until nine days before the Armistice was signed! This despite the fact that they commanded the outfit, acted as chiefs of its major departments, taught surgeons of incoming outfits war surgery, and in the Argonne Forest Battle saw the unit expanded until it had a staff of some seventy-five doctors and for weeks ran a daily census of some 1600 patients! Close up to the battle area, its status changed technically from a base to an evacuation hospital. Its surgeons among the most experienced in war surgery, the Hopkins outfit took, by order, only the heaviest battle casualties. Two million American troops were engaged.

Every other hospital group outranked that of the Hopkins by at least two numbers, and that is a little matter that has never been satisfactorily explained. I mention it because of the queer story that got around. Once the war got going in earnest, medical officers, like others, were stepped up in rank—those Hopkins men who had been taken away from the unit for higher duties included. Only the men who had been left holding the bag were forgotten. Commanding officers and chiefs of service of all big hospitals were lieutenant colonels (perhaps in a few only majors). Those manning the Hopkins remained captains. This despite the fact that Dr. Finney had put them in for promotion several times. It was about the only thing he tried to do and failed in.

Embarrassing though it was—especially so when it became necessary to instruct higher ranking men in the art of war surgery—the men carried on and even in the lodge made little complaint. There was a war, they were in it, what the hell! There was, however, a story—grapevine in character—and it was to the effect that too many men from the Hopkins had too much to say in the medical running of the A.E.F., and that certain parties (unknown) objected. With Dr. Finney Chief Consultant in Surgery, Dr. Thayer Chief Consultant in Medicine—both brigadier generals—with Hugh Young a colonel and in charge of Genitourinary Surgery, with Baer, Boggs, Walker, and others having less prominent positions and rank —although not much—I say, with this setup jealousies arose. Or so it was said. The fact that the men concerned were capable and did a good job, the fact that not all of them went over with the unit had no effect. There was objection, and somebody had to pay.

I do not vouch for the truth of the story. In some ways it is too fantastic to believe. Yet there was the fact that no man concerned with the actual running of the first hospital to arrive in France received promotion until the war was practically over. Not only that, when the last and biggest battle of all took place, and additional surgeons and physicians had to be allocated to the Hopkins, care had to be exercised by the medical authorities to see that no such men had rank higher than captain. Otherwise they would automatically have taken command and have been Chiefs of Service— supplanting the more experienced but lesser ranking men. When, nine days before the Armistice, promotion—one notch—did come, one of the high ranking men of the Surgeon General's office called up personally to tell of it—shamefacedly and with apologies.

Lest some might think that youth had something to do with it— youth of the men concerned and perhaps their comparative inexperience—the record shows that they were all in their late thirties (other than interns) and had had much clinical and scientific experience prior to going to France. In short, they were to be the wheel horses of the outfit—and they were. They had not expected to be the goats.

There was one awfully good story which illustrates the ridiculous thing in clear relief. Well along toward the war's end, when all the fighting was over, and Base No. 18 was resting on its laurels, a very doggy lieutenant colonel, Quartermaster Department, dropped into the office and, finding a captain there, said he wished to make an inspection. The captain thought it was strange, a Quartermaster officer inspecting a hospital, but he dutifully walked along, saying nothing and hardly being noticed. From ward to ward, inside and out, the lieutenant colonel went, not neglecting operating rooms, nurses' quarters, men's quarters, anything. He really inspected—all the time saying nothing. Coming at last to the kitchen and giving that the once over—cooks and helpers standing at attention—he suddenly turned to the doctor.

"Where's the colonel?" he said.

"How you mean colonel, sir?"

"The colonel! The colonel!" he barked. "The colonel commanding!"

"We got no colonel," the captain said. "You're looking at the commanding officer."

"Wha-a-at!" he shrieked. "Well, I'll be goddamned!" And with that he turned on his heel and left.

You should have heard the shouts the moment the poor man got out of earshot.

Two weeks later, word came that on inspection it was found that the personnel of Base No. 18 had one too many blankets on their beds, and would the C.O. see that they were removed. The C.O. wouldn't—and didn't.

We all know now that World War I was but the preview of World War II, and, of course, that went for all branches of the military—including the medical. Naturally I cannot speak for the other services, but two significant developments high-lighted the medical. One was the system of taking operating surgeons up to the heavily battle-wounded soldier instead of bringing him back to them as had previously been the custom, and the second was the introduction of blood transfusion on a grand scale. The Hopkins took part in both, more particularly the second. Dr. Finney disregarded a committee report that gave discretionary powers to doctors in three different methods and insisted that the then new and simple sodium citrate transfusion be the only one used. This marked the real beginning of blood transfusion on a major scale, and Americans have a right to be proud. They told the world—more particularly the British and French—and the world listened and followed the lead. For the first time in history, shock brought on by loss of blood and other things could be treated with confidence, and many wounded men, who otherwise must have died, lived. The sulfas and penicillin came some years after World War I, and so did plasma.

There were too many wonderful hospitals in France to say that any one of them was the ace unit of the A.E.F., but if the detailed record of Base No. 18 were laid before you, I think you would be much impressed. With the war's end and the unit's return to Baltimore, doctors resumed their former positions at the Hopkins—most of them comparatively minor—and it was business as usual. There were no advancements.

Chapter 24

WILMER EYE CLINIC

The Wilmer Institute for Diseases of the Eye was opened October 15, 1929, and was headed by the renowned Washington oculist, Dr. William Holland Wilmer. To do him honor his friends and former patients collected some $1,500,000 with the view to endowing a clinic that would combine research with practice. Presumably they were going to put it in the doctor's home city of Washington, D. C., but Dr. Welch convinced them that they hadn't sufficient funds for such elaborate plans as they had in mind and suggested that if they would cast their fortunes with the Hopkins, he would undertake to get more. The Hopkins had long contemplated an institute for eye diseases, and this was a golden opportunity. Dr. Wilmer would be made Professor, he would have his own staff, hospital, and laboratories, and all they needed was an additional $1,500,000. The Rockefeller Foundation supplied that, and with a total endowment of $3,000,000 the Wilmer Institute in short order became a valued and integral part of the Johns Hopkins Medical Center.

For the first time, patients afflicted with diseases of the eye could come to the Hopkins with the assurance of being properly hospitalized and treated. Not only that, laboratories were established in the institute, and men of special abilities were put in charge. Nothing of the kind had ever been known in America before, and up to this time no parallel has been developed. Patients and students alike promptly began taking advantage of the opportunities offered, and once again the Hopkins led the way. The Wilmer fitted in well with its other great and growing clinics, and the hospital especially was becoming the well-rounded institution people had always envisaged.

The old private pavilion for women to the left of the big main building of the Hopkins was rebuilt and enlarged to house the Wilmer. It has accommodations for seventy patients, an active outpatient department that handles some one hundred cases daily, and laboratories for clinical and research work. Doctors from far and

170

near come for instruction and to work on special problems, but equally important is the development of young men going on in the place. There is the usual house staff, mostly graduates of the Hopkins Medical School, and already quite a number of professorships in eye diseases in other American institutions have been filled from their ranks.

When Dr. Wilmer reached the age of retirement in 1933 he was succeeded by Dr. Alan Woods, who, with Dr. Jonas Friedenwald and other associates of similar distinction, carries on. Woods and Friedenwald are themselves Hopkins graduates, and so are many of their staff members, but not all. Studies have been carried out on the bacteriology of the eye—among other things—and Dr. Woods himself has devoted considerable time and attention to ocular tuberculosis.

I think it will be freely granted that the friends of Dr. Wilmer were wise in joining forces with the Rockefeller Foundation in establishing a more distinguished clinic at the Hopkins.

Chapter 25

WELCH INSTITUTE OF THE HISTORY OF MEDICINE

It BECAME a ritual at the Hopkins for Dr. Welch to conceive new adventures and direct them until they reached early childhood. I have no doubt that he had little difficulty with the School of Hygiene and more than likely he enjoyed starting it off, but the history of medicine had long been the great man's hobby, and he had real joy in establishing the institute that bears his name—first of its kind in America. If he could have had the lovable Osler with him, I dare say his cup of joy would have been filled. For Osler, too, was an ardent student of medical history and rarely lost an opportunity to stress its importance to those about him.

A rather interesting story is connected with founding the institute in that Dr. Welch seems first to have had only the idea of getting a department for the history of medicine—professorship and staff —with a suitable building for library and rooms for seminars. Not until he came up with Sudhoff—also Sigerist—in Leipzig and got an intimate view of what a real institute of medical history was like did it occur to him that a mere chair of history at the Hopkins was not enough. Karl Sudhoff had long been prominent in his field and although he had retired in favor of his young disciple, Henry E. Sigerist, he still retained his mental vigor and profoundly influenced all who came in contact with him—including Welch. Apparently this was the first time Welch and Sigerist had met. Their minds clicked immediately.

Perhaps I should say that the occasion of Dr. Welch's visit to Sudhoff was the trip he took abroad to study and buy books on medical history for the library. It was in May, 1927, that he sailed, following a $200,000 appropriation by the General Education Board in February, 1926, for endowment of the Chair for the History of Medicine, and later a gift by Edward S. Harkness of half a million dollars to complete the fund * for the William H. Welch Medical Library. On November 2, 1926, President Goodnow notified Welch

* Actually this fund was not completed until 1928.

officially of his transfer from other duties to Professorship of the History of Medicine, and from that moment on the doctor seems to have been imbued with the need, urgent and pressing, for personal study and investigation in his new field—however much he already knew about it.

Thus it is that we find him going on a trip that was to last well over a year, with no other idea than stocking his prospective library and orienting himself further in his new and somewhat unusual duties. To recite his trail up and down the paths and bypaths of Europe would be but an excursion into geography, and unusual geography at that—Padua, Leyden, Edinburgh, Carlsbad, Leiden, London, Zagreb, Budapest, Ragusa. In short, wherever there were men to talk to and libraries and institutes to see, he went, not overlooking bookstores great and small to browse in and maybe make purchases; operas, and meetings of medical historians to attend. When you think that at this time, 1927 and 1928, Dr. Welch was verging on eighty years of age, his youthful spirit and eager outlook all but take your breath away. They apparently affected his, too, at one period when (November 28) he went to Taormina for a month's rest rather than go on to Rome with the party he was then traveling with.

Naturally it wasn't Sudhoff alone who influenced the doctor toward his institute. The impact of other men—Arnold C. Kleb of Nyon, Switzerland, was a powerful one—and the many meetings he attended and things he saw must have been considerable. I only say that Sudhoff seems to have sowed the original seed, and this happened only a few short months after his arrival in Europe. He saw clearly that a mere Chair of Medical History without laboratory, assistants, museum, or students would be of little avail and, in any case, was not in keeping with his and the Hopkins's breadth of view. The idea of an institute for research was taking hold, and fate provided him an opening. Fate always seemed to be just around the corner with Welch. In August of that very year, 1927, he chanced to meet President Vincent of the Rockefeller Foundation and Abraham Flexner in Paris, and what more natural than that he should broach his new idea and ask for an endowment of $500,000 for the projected Institute of the History of Medicine! They were encouraging and suggested that when his plans were completed he lay them before the General Education Board which had already provided for his chair and was in process of contributing to the fund for his library building. The eminent doctor was no shrinking violet when he wanted something.

So Welch went ahead with his investigations and his purchases, and it is difficult to say which gave him the most pleasure. It is not difficult to say which got him into trouble or created some little pain and embarrassment. It was the purchases. The rotund little man got so interested that he forgot or neglected to keep records of what he bought, how much he paid for things, or apparently even where he got them all. After all, he was a doctor and not money-minded. But that wasn't all; he hadn't taken along with him to Europe a list of the books the Hopkins already had, and the list was rather long and pretentious. Why not? Hadn't he and Osler and Kelly and others of similar interests attended personally to the gathering of precious volumes, spending throughout the years such money as was available for the purpose? So he duplicated certain things and only realized it when they finally sent him the list from home. I guess it was then, too, that he became a bit worried over his expenditures and began counting up—such as he could remember! I can just see him smiling a little and maybe grinning a bit as he sat in some café, scanning the figures. I can't possibly see him seriously concerned. The Hopkins had given him $5,000 before he sailed, and the General Education Board, which he seems to have owned body and soul, expanded this up to $12,500. Before he got through, though, what with the various bills that began flooding in from here, there, and everywhere—many of the books were only remotely relevant to medicine—the amount he spent was close to $100,000, and maybe more!

On October 17 and 18, 1929, the Library and Department of the History of Medicine were officially dedicated with Harvey Cushing, Abraham Flexner, and Sudhoff making the principal addresses. The idea of the institute had taken time to percolate, and it wasn't until 1930 that the money was forthcoming. At that time the General

Education Board appropriated $250,000 as an endowment and added $12,500 to enable the eminent physician to carry out his ideas. On May 22, 1930, the nation and the world celebrated Dr. Welch's eightieth birthday, and it was then, with the President of the United States speaking, that he could truly say he had reached the heights of his institutional dreams. The ceremonies took place in Washington, and when President Hoover said, "Dr. Welch is our greatest statesman in the field of public health," scientists, educators, doctors, patients, and people the world over added a fervent "Amen."

As might be surmised, Dr. Welch was not so fatuous as to believe that a man of his years could initiate successfully and carry on a venture of such proportions as he had envisaged. With the skeleton staff he had engaged he did carry on for a time—giving weekly lectures on the history of British surgery, but within the year he evinced a desire to retire. He wanted Harvey Cushing to succeed him, but though Cushing was interested, he was too much occupied with his duties at Harvard to do so. The position was then offered to Charles Singer, distinguished British historian, but he, too, declined. Finally, with Welch's retirement becoming official on July 1, 1930, Fielding Garrison, historian and staff member, took over temporarily. The matter was not permanently resolved until May 1, 1932, at which time Henry E. Sigerist, whose success as a visiting lecturer had been so startling, accepted the proffered position. He took up his duties in the fall of that year, and only a few months later Dr. Welch himself wrote, "I think his coming to Johns Hopkins is one of the most important events in the history of the University for years." *

There will be those who disagree with the above statement, but I am not one of them. The institute has become a living, vital part of the Hopkins and the nation. Its endeavors roam far beyond pure medical history, encompassing as they do consideration and investigation into cultural activities of broad and varied importance, past, present, future. Men and women from this country and others come

* Flexner, Simon, and James Thomas Flexner, *William Henry Welch and the Heroic Age of American Medicine*, The Viking Press, Inc., New York, 1941.

to study and engage in research, while the students at the Hopkins evince avid interest. Sigerist fulfilled Dr. Welch's highest ambitions and more. His recent departure from the Hopkins after fifteen years of brilliant success—and at the early age of fifty-six—is painful to record. He said he wished to return to his native Switzerland for the quiet and leisure needed for special literary work. One may express the opinion that if Dr. Welch had lived, this would not have been necessary. Dr. Welch died in 1934 at the age of eighty-four.

Chapter 26

LOVE AND RUBBER GLOVES. HOPKINS NURSES

In a long and varied experience in the realm of medicine it has been my observation that training schools for nurses have two main objectives. They supply needed nurses for the hospitals with which they are associated, and wives for the doctors. The Johns Hopkins Training School excelled in both directions. Indeed, if we can believe history, it did more than that. Through one of its members it very early exerted significant practical and scientific effect on the development of surgery.

The member in question was the chief operating-room nurse of the eminent Professor Halsted, and it seems that the process then in vogue of scrubbing up for operations was too much for her hands and forearms. The chemical solutions (mercuric chloride) used after washing caused a skin irritation of such proportions as to make her life miserable, even to the point of incapacitation. The gallant Professor, who, by the way, had become enamored of the nurse, was much perturbed and, being of a scientific as well as utilitarian turn of mind, immediately proceeded to take steps looking toward overcoming the difficulty. He first conceived the idea of coating the skin with substances like collodion that would prevent the solutions from biting, but that did not work so well, and then, being driven by love as well as science, he had the brilliant idea that rubber gloves might afford the protection needed. Taking his problem to a salesman of the Goodyear Rubber Company, he had constructed thick, crude, loosely fitting things that weren't much to look at but answered all purposes. The gloves could be boiled, the fingers were big and easily entered, there were cuffs extending well up on the forearms, and even if the rubber was rather stiff, it did not seriously interfere with the duties performed by the nurse. This was along about 1890 to 1891. There seems to be some doubt about the exact date.

It seems that the Professor himself and the doctors associated with him at operations did not use the gloves, probably feeling that

177

their unwieldy proportions would interfere with delicate manipulations, but a young intern who merely handed instruments had no such compunctions. He, too, was having trouble with his skin, but it wasn't only from the so-called scrub-up solutions. There was another solution that he had to deal with—namely, carbolic acid—and trouble came from the custom of placing the boiled instruments in metal trays partially filled with this substance in dilution, in order to keep them from becoming contaminated by the air before and during operation. It was one of the duties of the instrument handler to wipe them more or less dry before giving them to the surgeon and his assistants, so that their bare hands and the patient's tissues would not be affected. What happened to the intern's hands, of course, was just one of those things that the boys took—until the advent of the nurse's gloves! *

Thus it was that the rubber gloves now universally used by surgeons throughout the world were born. It was love; love at Johns Hopkins. Nurse, intern, then assistants, and finally the Professor himself—in 1896—took to using the gloves, and before long better, more pliable, easier fitting, thinner ones were produced by the manufacturers, and from that moment, through that means, the art and science of surgery was immeasurably advanced. It remains only to be said that the original nurse—Miss Caroline Hampton—became Mrs. Halsted, and through her as well as others the Johns Hopkins Training School for Nurses has achieved undying fame.

I wouldn't say that it was the love element in the training school that made chief appeal to young ladies desiring to take up nursing at the Hopkins, but it is a fact that many of them married staff men in the early days, and the custom has persisted to greater or less degree on down through the years. And no wonder. Not only has there been a high degree of pulchritude among the nurses of the Johns Hopkins, there has been an equally high order of mentality and all that goes with it—education, culture, spirit, courage, above all the willingness to work and share experience. I cannot speak too highly of the women who took their training at the Hopkins, and it

* There are a number of variations to this story. One of them credits Dr. Bloodgood with being the assistant first to turn to the gloves.

happens that I have seen them under all sorts of conditions—including war and the bad, difficult times war makes, together with danger and work under battle conditions, air raids, and all.

This is not to say that the Hopkins nurses have a monopoly on all the virtues commonly attributed to members of their profession. It only means that they have their share and probably a little bit more, because of the fact that from the very beginning, standards for entrance into their school were higher than in the usual run of schools, and whether because of it or in spite of it, a superior type of student was obtained. They came from all over, including Canada, the latter being attracted no doubt by Dr. Osler and the numerous young Canadian students and doctors he influenced to join the Hopkins. This tendency of girls from Canada to train here has persisted and I think has been most helpful.

Because of the excellence of their training with emphasis on the scientific and the professional, also probably because of association with a medical school and hospital wherein quality and the reasoned, scientific approach are always held uppermost in mind, graduates of the Hopkins Training School for Nurses have tended to become teachers, supervisors, and administrators rather than individual practitioners. I think this is a logical development, and it is not to be doubted that their influence has been widespread throughout the nation. This isn't to say that there aren't Hopkins nurses occupied with the practical duties of tending the individual sick. I dare say the majority of them are, but if you looked closely, you probably would find that they produce a greater proportion of supervisors than other schools.

The school has recently raised its requirements for entrance still higher. It has demanded a college degree of all aspirants, thus making it a graduate school and putting it on a level with that of the Medical School. Obviously, this step was taken with the avowed purpose of developing none but teachers, supervisors, and administrators. One could hardly expect women who have spent long years learning the theory of their profession and studying nursing from the scientific angle, with all that that implies, going forth as private-duty nurses to do the various and varied practical and menial things of the lesser trained. It would be sheer waste of time and energy and, if the truth were known, they would hardly be as adept at it as the others. You don't learn the practical things in classrooms and you don't need so much theory and science to do them, either.

There has been no little criticism of the Hopkins school for taking this action. With the nurse situation throughout the nation critical because of the shortage of trained personnel, it is said that the need is not for higher education of nurses but for less; not for more of the scientific among them but for more of the practical; not for the prolonged three or four years' study but for six months or, at most, one year's preparation. By its action of arrogating to itself the graduate-school type, critics say the Hopkins institution is making a bad situation worse, that other schools will follow the example set, and the nurse shortage will become even more acute. Worse still, by elevating the profession of nursing to such a high plane there is danger of forgetting or neglecting the little practical things that are so important in tending the sick in favor of the scientific and theoretical. Finally, it is said that through this higher education nurses tend more to become doctors or to assume the duties of doctors, and that should not be within their sphere. Better leave that to the doctors themselves and specially trained technicians.

I think myself that the critics are mistaken, or perhaps have not thought the thing through. But I also think the Hopkins authorities have a bit more thinking to do, too. There is no doubt in my mind that the modern development of medicine demands far greater and more fundamental training of teachers, supervisors, and administrators of nursing than ever before. That being so, I think no more logical place for that to be given could be found than the Hopkins school—and schools of similar character and quality. By the very token, though, of need for greater education in the upper nurse echelons, with emphasis on special knowledge, there should be concomitant recognition of need for less theoretical education in the lower echelons, with emphasis on short-time training in the practical, everyday duties that go with care of the sick.

In other words, there is need for an officer personnel in the nursing profession, but there is equal, even greater, need for a private-soldier personnel to carry out their orders. The Hopkins has all along trained officers chiefly. Now they are going to train them exclusively and better. To make them efficient, to balance things, they should forthwith inaugurate in addition the other type of school—that for the nurses in the ranks, six months' intensive basic training—at most, a year. Not only would the Hopkins thus be setting the example, by having this secondary school they would be in position to give their officer personnel practical training in command and field-work direction.

In another book * I have gone into this matter of officer and private-soldier nurse personnel more in detail, but it might not be amiss to say here that the time has come for the nurse problem in the United States to be looked squarely in the face. It is most unsatisfactory; it gets steadily worse; something must be done about it. The causes are many and varied and cannot be gone into here, but if one thing is clear, it is that young girls of this day and generation are not going to spend three long years getting training that could be given them in six months. No one believes in education more than I do, but I've been a doctor too long and have seen too much to believe that most sick people need more than the small practical things any person with common sense could give them. Only the minority need the special care that can be given solely by the highest trained, and there should be little difficulty in supplying that. In days gone by, when colleges and the business world weren't open to girls, and girls weren't on to themselves as they are now, about the only way they could get away from home was to go into nursing. That was their chief gate to freedom, and they submitted to the three-year course, which was exploitation really, because it was either that or nothing.

The picture has now changed, and the medical and nursing professions had best see it clearly. The "call" that they talked about so glibly was little more than lip service at best. It has gone now, and reality has taken its place. If people who get sick are going to

* Bernheim, Bertram M., *A Surgeon's Domain*, W. W. Norton & Company, New York, 1947.

have nursing care from here on, they are going to get it on a different basis, for which purpose there will have to be two different classes of trained personnel. I have indicated them. I would say that the nation needs not less than 1,000,000 trained nurses— one-fifth officers, four-fifths soldiers in the ranks. I see no reason why the bigger, more important institutions shouldn't have both types of schools. In fact, I see every reason why they should. As for the others, they should have but the one—that for the privates— and I think practically all of them have or could be provided with staffs that could teach them. Larger hospitals could have larger schools; smaller, outlying ones could have smaller ones—schools maybe that would turn out but five or ten graduates at a time. I don't see why standards should be the same in them, either. In fact, it occurs to me that we have been looking upon nursing in too stereotyped a manner, and maybe the rules will have to be considerably revamped.

I call these matters to the attention of the Hopkins authorities, feeling that a glorious opportunity lies within their grasp. I recognize the difficulties and have no doubt that one of them concerns the State Boards of Examination. Rules, regulations, and standards will have to be changed to fit the two classes of nurses. Another concerns granting diplomas and the dangers inherent in women of the two categories going out as Hopkins nurses. This latter is real and, in the end, may prevent the Hopkins and similar institutions from having the two types of schools. I hope not. It would seem to me that a way could be found to designate graduates of the one school, Doctors of Nursing, and graduates of the other, Trained Nurses. Certainly the graduates of the higher school should have the title "Doctor Nurse."

Chapter 27

THE HOPKINS BETWEEN WARS. DETERIORATION? MISTAKES?

IT HAS BEEN exceedingly difficult to get the exact formula for the period between World War I and World War II. The trouble arises from the fact that the Hopkins underwent significant change during those years. It was a gradual, subtle change that manifested itself chiefly in a sort of leveling-off process characteristic of anything new, once the adjustment period is over, but it was definite and requires consideration and explanation. Some men talk of the "period of lowest ebb at Hopkins" and put it roughly between the years 1923 and 1938, at which time they say a gradual improvement became perceptible.

There are those, and they are many, who are of the opinion that once the original Four Physicians became less active and then faded out of the picture completely, the Hopkins promptly began to deteriorate. I do not agree *in toto*. It wasn't so much a deterioration of the Hopkins as it was an upsurge of other medical institutions, due in no small part to the Hopkins influence and example. The Hopkins lost only some of its unique character and perhaps a little of its momentum. It became more of a first-class fine institution of learning unlit by the stellar luminaries of earlier days.

This doesn't mean that problems arising were all well handled, that every appointment was up to the previous high standard, or that the same imagination and spirit as of old were in evidence. That would be too much to expect, and I, for one, don't think they were. It merely means that the over-all picture remained essentially the same, that the same idealistic aims generally continued to prevail, and patients and doctors alike, also medical students, could continue to come to the Hopkins and find things going on in usual fashion. The chief difference was that whereas those who came previously were drawn by the magnet of great names, now they were largely or increasingly drawn by the institution itself. Without doubt there remained the occasional standout who drew doctors and patients to himself and the institution in a manner similar to that of the early masters—Walter Dandy, renowned brain surgeon and successor to Cushing, was one, and from time to time others appeared on the horizon. The present incumbent of the Chair of Surgery, Blalock, with his special operation for "blue babies"— congenital heart disease—is a case in point. But generally speaking, the years between the wars saw a gradual falling away from the individual giant in medicine—not only at the Hopkins but at the Mayo Clinic and elsewhere—and the rise of the institution itself and the many in his place. The change was occasioned by the more general "spread" of medical knowledge coupled with broad scientific advance. With the exception of some particular discovery by the individual or development of a device, a special test, the day was done when one doctor towered above those about him, and in its place came the day of cooperative effort, the teamwork that is so necessary and that we now see in medicine.

It is of extreme importance for the understanding of things at the Hopkins that this be clearly understood and kept in mind. The change did not come in a day or a month or a year. It was a very gradual, almost imperceptible development, and that is why I say the difference at the Hopkins was subtle. You couldn't put your finger on any one thing, yet you sensed that a change was coming over the place. Without thinking too deeply, some men concluded that the institution was fading, and rather badly at that, but they were mistaken. It was only undergoing the metamorphosis of modernization. If they had seen things with clarity and understanding, they would have realized how odd and unusual it would have been for real deterioration to have set in so soon. That could only have meant—if it had happened—that the great men who started the Hopkins left little of lasting value and were not the supermen the medical profession and people generally thought they were. No one believed that then, and no one does now.

In all likelihood the thing that first created disquiet over the Hopkins—and made it suspect—was the trouble incurred in filling Professorships in its two key departments of Medicine and Surgery. The one happened immediately after the war, the other a few short years later—in 1922, when Dr. Halsted died. You will recall my saying that when the Hopkins first embarked on the system of "full time" for clinical medicine—around 1912—it was too soon, and the war saved it. The authorities didn't push the matter further at the time, but they maintained their gains and apparently felt secure in their position until an unexpected and cruel blow befell them. Dr. Theodore C. Janeway had a change of heart. It was he who had come down from New York so eagerly to take the Chair of Medicine which Barker had vacated. A clinician of outstanding ability and importance, thoroughly imbued with the virtue of the full-time system, it was with no small satisfaction that the Hopkins directorate had welcomed him. Yet here he was, only two or three years later, changing his mind completely and resigning his professorship. The fact that he got the flu in 1917 and died of pneumonia before his successor could be named only added poignancy to his defection and the causes thereof.

Certain desirable men refused the position, and a period of interregnums followed. Among others, Dr. Thayer held it for a time but he was unhappy and gave it up. Nor was the situation improved when, a few years later, a similar state of affairs came to pass with regard to the surgical department. Dr. Finney was among those who were offered Halsted's chair, but he didn't believe in the full-time system, in the first place, and, in the second place, felt that he couldn't afford it. His two years in the Army had weighed heavily on his financial resources, and that, coupled with his unsympathetic attitude, made his decision definite. He headed the department for two years, finally turning it over to Dean Lewis. Warfield Longcope became Professor of Medicine. Rumor had it that he was by no means the first choice.

Longcope was a Hopkins graduate who had gone to New York and made his mark at Columbia University. He was a natural for his new position in that he had never practiced and was wholeheartedly in favor of full time. In addition, he was a Baltimorean with a background of culture, refinement, and erudition. He had, in fact, every quality desirable save one—or at most two or three. He lacked color and fire; he was overly modest; he was too retiring; and as the years rolled by he did not frequent the usual medical meetings and make himself and the Hopkins known and liked. Scholar, investigator, teacher, clinician he was, and his men say he was also a good executive. He organized his department well and kept it in high gear. Some students thought him good and liked him. Others didn't. Most of those I talked to respected him but felt that he was too aloof.

"You can't get at him," one man said.

"Got no warmth," another one remarked.

"But plenty of stuff," said a third, "only he doesn't shove it at you. You've got to make some effort yourself."

His residents swore by him and not a few of them became well known and highly regarded in their various spheres. In short, Longcope ably upheld the best traditions of Osler, Thayer, and Barker; he initiated much medical work that was new; he built men and gave them their heads—yet. . . . It was the "yet" that made people—and certain doctors—feel that his appointment had been a mistake. They recalled the buoyant, colorful Osler and couldn't see Longcope alongside of him or trying to fill his niche. They didn't stop to think that Oslers are the rarest of men and that even near approaches aren't easy to find—that is, near approaches who have the other things Osler had besides color. Whatever opportunity the directorate had, though, of getting an older, well-established clinician who had everything was completely nullified by their insistence on his going on "full time." That kind of man was bound to refuse—in those days, anyhow—and I should say that they were extremely lucky in getting a man who had as much and as high quality as Longcope.

With Lewis it was different. I think they made a mistake—and did Lewis a great injustice. He was a fine man but he never should have become Professor of Surgery at the Hopkins. Like Longcope, it appears that he was not the first or even the second choice. Rumor had several men of note being sounded out. I see no point in mentioning names other, perhaps, than Harvey Cushing who, Fulton says, definitely declined.* Lewis finally got the call and accepted,

* Fulton, John F., *Harvey Cushing: A Biography*, Charles C. Thomas, Publisher, Springfield, Ill., 1946.

but many of us couldn't understand why. We finally came to the conclusion that it must have been the name and general glamour and prestige of the Hopkins that provided the overwhelming attraction. He had been an intense admirer of Dr. Halsted. Professor of Surgery at Chicago, one of the most successful surgeons of that city—perhaps the most successful, and as a result, a man of considerable means—at fifty-six years of age Lewis probably saw himself filling the greatest of all surgical chairs in the nation with distinction. And so he would, if that chair had been anything but what it was—the pinnacle of investigative work and philosophical thought, with the practical coming in only as an aid to them. The great Halsted had so ordained. That is how the Hopkins as an institution regarded it. Lewis was not the type.

I never thought Lewis was comfortable or entirely happy at the Hopkins. He was out of his natural element. Hail fellow well met, typical Middle Westerner, he liked nothing better than to talk sports and attend them—in and out of the city. Baseball was a prime favorite, but he liked them all. He knew personally many leaders of sports, mostly professional, and many came to Baltimore to consult him. Staunch supporter of the American Medical Association, he became its president. Between attendance at sports events and medical meetings Lewis was away from Baltimore almost as much as he was home. In that respect he was the exact opposite of Longcope.

He was an editor of medical journals and had an almost encyclopedic knowledge of the literature, yet he had done comparatively little original investigative work and apparently was not greatly interested in it. Under him the Hunterian Laboratory of Experimental Surgery mostly drifted along an undistinguished course. Primarily, Lewis was a clinician and a teacher of distinction. He was interested in all practical surgery but seemed to like that associated with the nerves best. These were all valuable attributes, but unfortunately for him they were not the ones on which Hopkins men laid the greatest stress. The investigative, the philosophical, the spiritual values, the individual delving, all traditional after Halsted, left the new professor cold, but he never made pretense of them, and that's why I say those who chose Lewis and persuaded him to come to the Hopkins did him an injustice, as well as the Hopkins. They should have known he was not the man they wanted. Many of us did, but we weren't consulted. We had known Dr. Lewis before the war, during it in France, where he had a distinguished career, and afterwards again in Chicago. No one was more surprised than we were when word came that he was to be the professor.

Sometimes I thought he was sorry himself, and it was on that basis, chiefly, that one could understand his failure to organize his department properly. He was overwhelmed with the difficulties of the task he had assumed and so lost interest and even crept into a sort of protective shell. Like Longcope, he inherited a staff of loyal, highly trained, well-regarded men, but, unlike Longcope, he could not bring himself to give them responsibilities and duties in accordance with their merits. Most especially did he fail to take suggestions that might have brought him and the institution acclaim. I refer particularly to the representations made to establish a clinic for peripheral vascular diseases, one for plastic surgery, and possibly something in the nature of a special department for surgical affections of the rectum. That was the time for the Hopkins to branch out importantly in those fields—already valuable time had been lost, but it wasn't too late—and there was little doubt that adequate support, financial and otherwise, could have been gotten, but Lewis flatly refused to hear of them.

I think we are all too prone to magnify passing phases in which we take part ourselves and to let them color our viewpoint and affect our judgment of the over-all picture. I know that happened to me. When I saw opportunities lost in my own department and heard men from other departments griping about the inequities and shortcomings of theirs, I came definitely to the conclusion that the Hopkins was going rapidly to hell. And when I went to medical meetings and talked to doctors from other institutions—some Hopkins alumni, some not—and heard them laughing and joking about the men who had been offered professorships at the Hopkins and refused them, I was shocked. To make matters worse, they told of new departures recently established at their places and frequently ended up by asking, "Who did take the Professorship of Medicine at Hopkins, anyhow?"

They never asked who took the Professorship of Surgery because Lewis was always on hand and usually reading a paper or making a few remarks, but not a few of them smiled and asked brazenly if the Hopkins people thought he was another Halsted.

It all burned deep and affected my better judgment—as I think it did that of others. No institution, no business house, ever proceeds on even keel always, and temporary stalemate in one department— for whatever cause—does not necessarily spell ruin. There is usually sufficient reserve to make up for a weak link and carry it along until substitutions or replacements can be made. And that was what was happening at the Hopkins, only it was handicapped by custom with regard to replacements. Death alone could bring that about— other than resignation, and rare it is in any institution of learning for the latter to happen. The university appointee of the upper professorial level is practically always for life—or until the age of retirement. Even when the written note says "one year and renewal each year," it doesn't mean it. Not, at least, at the Hopkins. I have never known them to let out a professor at the Medical School.

There is, or was—it has changed a bit—good reason for permanent tenure of office in the institution of learning. It is different with business. The business executive isn't necessarily hurt when he drops out or is pushed. Somehow or other he usually gets as good a job or even a better one. Maybe not always, but usually. Unless, of course, there has been some glaring lapse. That is not so with the university man. You throw a man out, and he's usually a dead duck, whether you talk or not. The man of established reputation wouldn't dream of giving up a secure position on anything but a permanent basis. Not if he was in his right mind he wouldn't. It might be different with the man not yet established, and I rather think the coming years, with the switch to younger men of potentialities rather than of completed accomplishments, might well see them willing to sign up on the basis of retention *if they make good.* It would make for a healthier situation, and there would be more of a tendency for men to keep alive and working instead of becoming complacent and dying on their feet by reason of security. An earlier retirement age—of, say, fifty, certainly sixty—might even work out still better. Most men of science have shot their bolt long before those years. They should not be relegated to the old folks' home, but should merely give way to younger and more alert men while assuming other, less directional, types of work.

Thus you see why Dr. Lewis stayed on at the Hopkins. I don't think anyone was particularly happy, but I don't think, either, that his tenure of office did permanent harm, although his failure to see the advisability of establishing new and desirable clinics cannot be laughed off. There was always his staff. He died at the age of sixty-five—nine years after he took over.

It is worth noting that this whole episode could have been avoided if the Hopkins authorities had been less rigid in their adherence to plan. At bottom I suppose it must be laid at the door of Dr. Welch, because he it was who not only foisted "full time" on the Hopkins but insisted on maintaining it. Not only that, he was impatient with dissenters, and there were many of those among the clinical men. Especially among those who had been to war. They returned considerably changed, much less willing to be dominated—even by Dr. Welch. Whereas before they usually sat quietly saying nothing at the few meetings they were asked to attend and permitted themselves to be told, now they asked questions, entered into argument, and said their piece—pleasantly and with respect—but definitely and without fear of consequences. Dr. Welch was surprised and, I thought, much chagrined. Upon one occasion he was very sharp with the group and lost his temper, something most unusual for him. Yet no man changed his opinion. For the record it should be noted that at no time did Dr. Finney attempt to influence others to his way of thinking. He didn't need to. The clinical staff men of that day in surgery were practically a unit in opposing full time.

From this brief recitation I think you can see that in the years between the wars, certain imponderables were importantly entering the picture at the Johns Hopkins, and that essentially they were of artificial creation. There can be little doubt that some of the fire and color was gone from the institution—how could it be otherwise?—and that to a certain extent it was running on its initial momentum. One could not escape the feeling that a lowered staff morale had ensued. You cannot expect men to keep on their toes if they are not in sympathy with general policies and if they see only clouded futures ahead.

It was the combination of these circumstances, well bruited about, that contrived to give the impression that the Hopkins was slipping —a little matter that apparently never reached the ears of the directing genius, Dr. Welch, and indeed he would have been the least concerned if it had. His mind was too much occupied with other matters, notably the Wilmer Institute for Diseases of the Eye and the Institute for the History of Medicine, both of which were established during this period of so-called desuetude.

I have often wondered why he didn't lay plans for a neurological institute at the same time. What with the distinguished Cushing and his successor, the brilliant Walter Dandy, the Hopkins had had two of the greatest brain surgeons who ever lived, and it would seem to have been a "natural." Easier to get and more logical, if not more necessary, than either of the other two institutes. Yet we heard nothing of it, and nothing came to pass. I am inclined to think a clinic of that type would have been more convincing to doubters than any other single gesture that could have been made—but who at the Hopkins wanted to be convincing? Nobody was alarmed.

Chapter 28

THE HOPKINS MEDICAL GRADUATE.
CONSIDERATION OF OBJECTIVES

I CONCEIVE IT to be the prime duty of a medical school to teach men and women to be doctors. In the matter of evaluation you have to keep objectives constantly before you. The Johns Hopkins Hospital, the great laboratories of the Medical School, the different clinics— all these had for their chief purpose the education in medicine of the students. Whatever else was accomplished, however important or startling, must be regarded in the light of accessory or by- product. It is different with an institute like the Rockefeller; it is different with a clinic like Mayo, and I do not think I have to elucidate. Neither has students in process of being made doctors. Even medical schools may have some variation in objectives. The one like Hopkins—also a few others—points its men more to teaching and scientific effort; the other—like the University of Maryland, in fact most medical schools—points its men toward practice or at least the practical side of medicine. I do not over- look the care and treatment of patients who come to the hospitals associated with medical schools. That, too, in the broadest sense, must be regarded as accessory.

I make this point and stress it because so many doctors—many of them alumni—base their arguments concerning the Hopkins's "slip- ping" on a false thesis.

"They're doing nothing down there," they say.

"What are they producing?" they argue. "Look at the new stuff being turned out elsewhere. The Hopkins used to be in the fore- front, but—"

"You don't hear of the place like you used to."

And more to the same effect.

Without doubt some will regard what I am saying in the light of a defense, and in a way maybe it is, though I look at it as an explanation of what has happened in the years between the wars. The matter of lower accomplishments in the field of research

harped on by most critics amounts to little more than broad general-
izations and vulnerable guesses. They never try to bring proof by
recitation of deeds performed or not performed, and I do not intend to try that, either. It would be out of place in a work of this
sort in the first place, and would be too formidable in the second
place. In addition, it would require a superscientist, and at best
would be but one man's opinion. What I think they refer to is
possibly a lack of startling effects such as Cushing and Halsted,
and maybe Hugh Young and Kelly and Abel produced. But what
they forget is that medicine and surgery have changed, the field
isn't nearly so unplowed as it formerly was, and other than the
newer drugs and chemicals you don't see the drama you used to—
generally speaking, that is. At Hopkins or any place else. The day
of the "towering man" in medicine is mostly done. Those who were
so used to seeing and hearing big things coming from the Hopkins
express surprise at not seeing and hearing a continuation without
considering the reasons.

Yet there has not been a complete dearth even of the spectacular—
as note the work done on the sulfas. They were discovered abroad,
but it was at the Hopkins that the first broad-gauged clinical application in this country was made. Perrin Long with Eleanor Bliss,
of Longcope's department, carried out exceptionally careful and
exhaustive experiments and observations, thereby putting these
extraordinary agents on a firm basis.* And Ken Marshall, pharmacologist, pupil and successor to the renowned John J. Abel, col-
laborated with them beautifully, even to the extent of discovering
sulfaguanidine,† a new and less toxic derivative. You can't always
be at the head of the procession, and in research, timing and luck
and lots of other things play a part. But you can be alert and have
your eye on the ball, and the exploits just related speak volumes
for the men of Hopkins. The sulfas lay dormant a long time before

* Long, Perrin H., and Eleanor A. Bliss, *The Clinical and Experimental Use
of Sulphanilamide and Sulphapyridine and Allied Compounds*, The Macmillan
Company, New York, 1939.

† Fairley, Brigadier N. Hamilton, "Medicine in Jungle Warfare," *Proceed-
ings of the Royal Society of Medicine*, 38:195, 1945.

coming alive, and the same thing is true of penicillin. The men of the Hopkins had a share in developing both.

But it isn't these things that concern me at the moment because, as noted, they are not the true gauge of a medical school. The true gauge is the character of the main product, and the main product of the medical school is the doctor. I see no falling off of the Hopkins man's stature. He remains as always a well-trained, thoughtful man (or woman, of course) with emphasis on the scientific. If I had to criticize him at all, I'd say that he is too much imbued with the scientific for his own good, but that is only a passing phase. He soon learns that it doesn't pay to see medical ills and patients *entirely* through the eyes of tests and test tubes, microscopes, pathological sections, X rays, and abstruse science, and very early begins to adjust himself. Despite the fact that he has seen and dealt with patients in the dispensaries and in the wards of his alma mater, when he becomes an intern it comes to him with a shock that there are people in the world and that patients are people and that the personal and social loom large in most of their ailments. So he begins to look at his attitude anew.

Especially is he perplexed to find that the vast majority of patients are not so very ill to start with, and mostly have the commoner affections about which he knows little or nothing. They figure at the Hopkins that if the student doesn't see the rarer things during his course and learn about them firsthand, he probably never will. Which may be true and all right, but it works a hardship on the boy when he goes out to meet the world. He gets pushed around something awful, and the little squirts from medical schools of lower standards who aren't fit to shine his shoes take great glee in doing most of the pushing. I know because I was chief surgeon of two hospitals separate and distinct from the Hopkins and director of one of them where opportunity aplenty was presented for observation. In addition, and because of my not being a native Baltimorean, I had opportunity more than lots of others to observe the poor Hopkins youngster outside of Baltimore.

It was sheer delight to see how he handled himself—generally speaking, of course. With rare exceptions he took his "medicine" with good humor and well it was that he did, because he usually was terrible. He couldn't put on a bandage and if he did it wouldn't stay on. He knew little of the commoner drugs and less of dosage. In the accident room he acted dazed, and the little guy ran circles around him, making the lame and the halt and the blind who were dragged in comfortable, soothing them and doing all the hundred and one things practical people with a practical bent do so well. All the Hopkins man could do was think of the rarer thing the poor souls could have but didn't and rush to the laboratories to make tests. He was always hell on tests. He couldn't bring himself to use his eyes and ears and hands and heart like the other fellows —not, that is, until he'd been knocked off repeatedly and had his face rubbed into the dirt of misunderstanding and misinterpretation.

Then he began to perk up and take notice. You could see him listening and watching and learning the little things that are so big and important in the aggregate. He asked questions and wasn't averse to taking advice. From anybody—doctor, nurse, orderly, technician—the patient himself. It was wonderful to watch him grow up and get wise. Many is the time I could have helped but didn't.

"Let him work out his own salvation," I said to myself. "That's in his blood. He'll be all the better for it."

And the interesting thing about it was that he could be practical and use common sense the moment he began to shed part of his scientific crust and put his mind to it. It was the same with all the fellows who came from the superior medical schools of the more scientific bent. They all went through the fire ordeal and mostly came out better men. I just was more interested in the fellow from the Hopkins and, truth to tell, I really think he was the "babe in arms" more than the others. Sometimes he'd curry favor by doing a bit of teaching—surreptitiously usually, because the practical boys didn't like to admit weakness—and in that manner learn the facts of life, medically speaking. You'd see him working in the laboratory with a fellow who was shaky there but strong in the outpatient clinic, and if you watched closely, you'd see them going over ward cases together with the Hopkins man doing most of the talking—books alongside for reference. It took weeks generally for this to happen. The boys had to become acquainted and take each other's measure, after which the trading began.

After six months the Hopkins man began to catch on—in my experience it took him that long—and from there on in he was a changed man and a better one. He was more humble and more tolerant of the other man's shortcomings—much less given to sounding off and telling them "how we do things at the Hopkins." More than any other one thing, that was what irked and bored the other fellows most, I thought. The constant repetition of "at Hopkins" or "the way Dr. So-and-so at Hopkins looked at it"—Hopkins, Hopkins, Hopkins, *ad nauseam.* Occasionally I'd take a man aside and tell him to pipe down. He bored me, too. And then there were the other little things: mannerisms like smiling superciliously and looking wise when another man failed to mention the rarer things in discussing the possibilities of cases on ward rounds. Certain Hopkins men were unpopular because they couldn't seem to get over that.

In six months the smart ones had gotten wise; in nine months they were even with the others; in twelve months they usually were forging ahead and giving advice to their mates—but always guardedly and by that time only when asked. By that time, too, the staff men had begun to seek them out a bit. As a general rule, the non-Hopkins staff men didn't like the intern from Hopkins at first. In fact, they disliked him—and feared him a little. More than one man made complaint.

"That Hopkins fellow of yours. . . ." It was always "my" Hopkins fellow, as if I somehow was entirely responsible and to blame for his shortcomings.

"That Hopkins fellow of yours," they'd say, "is a damned smart aleck and has too much to say."

I'd smile. The pattern was always the same.

"Gives too much advice without being asked and is eternally trying to make something unusual and complicated out of something simple. Cripes, what he don't know—"

"Give him a chance," I'd say soothingly, "and try to understand him. He isn't showing off. That's all the poor simp knows—the rare and unusual."

And then the wrath would flare forth.

"You mean to stand there and tell me that all they teach the boys at Hopkins is this aleukemic leukemia stuff and Banti's disease and sympathetic nervous system stuff—things you never come up with on the outside and usually miss when you do?"

"Yep. That's about all. I'm the only one over there that's got any common sense, and they won't listen to me."

That always brought a laugh and helped smooth down ruffled feathers.

"Well, I'll be—"

"They do sort of show him how to go about finding things out for himself, though," I'd then add. "And they like to have him say what he thinks—" but by that time the complainant was walking down the corridor, shaking his head. He'd usually turn, though, and come back.

"I will say this," he'd add as an afterthought, "the guy isn't afraid of work. Fact is, he's a workin' fool and is always running to get a book or make some test. He'll sit up half the night looking up some minor point or give up a date to watch a patient. Craziest fellow I ever saw."

As I say, that was the usual pattern. It took the other interns to sort of cool the Hopkins man off and give him a good going over before he came down from the clouds and became human. Until that time the staff men didn't get him and frequently made his life miserable—mine, too—with their carping criticisms. More than once it got so that I had to take a fellow aside for a going over of my own.

"Listen, Johnny," I'd say, "you've got to remember that this isn't the Hopkins Hospital, and these staff and visiting men are mostly not Hopkins men. Don't tell 'em so much."

"Yes, sir. But if they ask?"

"You've got to know your man. Some of them ask your opinion but only want it if it agrees with theirs."

"Wha-a-t!"

"That's it, and if you're going to get along here you've got to know people—especially doctors. Some of them are shy, believe it or not, and want your opinion regardless, but hesitate to ask for it because they think it makes them look bad—unlearned. Others ask and want it no matter what and they are the most tolerant and honest and usually the best ones. Some men want interns to be seen and not heard; they like 'em to do as they're told and shut up. You gotta size up your man."

"Yes, sir. Thank you, sir. Nobody ever told me such things before."

And then there was another one who was so upstage he was unbearable. I really had to take him on my knee.

"Look, Freddie. You're a smart boy but dumber 'n hell just the same. For God's sake stop twirling that Phi Beta Kappa key around when you talk to people. In fact, throw it away or lock it up. People around here will get your number without your telling 'em how bright you are. And don't you let me hear you again ask Dr. Green abstruse questions that you know he can't answer. It ain't smart, and for your information he's a damned good doctor. He could teach you lots if you had sense enough to cotton up to him and listen. Not everybody has to go to the Hopkins to be a good man, and some who do aren't nearly as good as they think they are."

But he wouldn't learn. He told one of his mates that I'd never made Phi Beta Kappa—which was true—so I couldn't know what it meant to be the proud possessor of a key. Last time I heard of him he was still twirling the key—and getting nowhere.

I should say that staff men who were patient and willing to overlook little foibles were well repaid. They got something from the Hopkins man they didn't get from the others, though they didn't always know exactly what it was or appreciate it. It was intelligent discussion of their cases with mutual exchange of ideas and opinions —the intern's being more bookish and theoretical, the staff man's more practical. Thus many doctors who started out disliking the boys from Hopkins ended up by liking them and being their staunchest supporters when it came to choosing the man to stay on and become assistant resident. And more than one Hopkins graduate that I knew owed his whole future to a non-Hopkins graduate who couldn't abide him at first.

Contrariwise, the Hopkins man was quick to size up the staff doctor and visiting men generally. Instinctively they'd sense whether a fellow knew his stuff or not, whether he was bluffing and putting on an act. The occasional one would poke fun at him and deliberately trip him up, but generally speaking they'd let him alone and devote their attentions to more sincere men. Favors, invitations did not seem to influence them, and that in itself speaks volumes because a certain element of the medical profession uses that method to gain the good will of house officers to which their talents and actions do not entitle them.

Finally, I should say that the Hopkins graduate usually knew better than most young men what he wanted of medicine and from the beginning pointed to it. He frequently came for advice and counsel as to means and methods but rarely, in my experience, as to objective. His mind was fixed on that beforehand. He only wanted to know how best to reach it—and as a rule didn't much care how long it took. I have known men who hadn't a dime in their jeans plan a course that took years, and it was rare that they let anything divert them. They'd borrow money, the occasional one married a wealthy girl who could see him through (or whose parents could); somehow they'd find ways and means. Where possible they'd work during their vacations, but vacations were so short it wasn't possible to do much. Some got scholarships of one sort or another. I should say that the majority married and married early—while students, or shortly after, while house officers. Their wives practically always worked, and so they managed, but I often thought they had rough going and for years were miserable if not downright unhappy. Most of those I knew personally were smart enough not to have children, but some began raising families immediately, and upon occasion their plight necessitated change of plans in spite of them.

As one would expect, it was the scientific that made chief appeal. They had an insatiable desire for learning. They wanted to do research. They wanted to become specialists. Few of them wished to be plain physicians. Many of them did, of course, because eventually responsibilities and finances forced them into it, but they usually had it in the back of their minds to become consultants, and many of them succeeded. Whatever branch they went into, though, they did it with the utmost seriousness, and over and above residencies in hospitals they'd take special preparatory courses and travel a bit. Those who could afford it went to Europe—also some who couldn't. The interesting thing about it was that the element of time was completely ignored. It was preparation, study, more preparation, special work. Many times I thought they overdid it, but after I had gently said so a few times and been politely snubbed I never did it again. I thought they'd be better off if they got started on their life's work first—after good training, of course—and took up further special study, even research, a few years later. By this means they would get a little practical knowledge and could better appraise their future needs. But if you've ever tried to argue with a graduate of the Hopkins Medical School, you'll know how futile it is, and if you haven't, you'll soon find out if you try. I really should have known better.

It would serve no useful purpose to give the proportion of Hopkins men engaged in teaching, research, and practice in comparison with men from other institutions—it might even do harm—but whatever it is, I wouldn't think it has changed materially. I see no falling off in his stature. He's the same fine type he always was, and wherever you go you find him highly regarded.* That isn't to say that there aren't unworthy sons or failures. There are. It merely means that for the most part the product from the Hopkins is still high quality. As for the rest, if you feel that there haven't been the books coming from staff men at the Hopkins—like those of Osler, Howell, Whitridge Williams, Kelly, Hugh Young, and others— I might agree with you. If you feel that the men who manned the

---

* It should be noted that some men think the caliber of doctor turned out by medical schools *generally* during the war years leaves something to be desired. They hold that the accelerated course is responsible. I personally think time alone will tell.

guns at the Hopkins between World War I and World War II were less colorful than their predecessors and not quite up to their stature, there, too, I might agree with you. But I feel compelled to say that "it was a big order," and all things considered, one that was impossible to fill. I think I have proved that they have manfully done what was expected of them in regard to the *product*, and that alone is deserving of high praise.

Finally, I should say that never again will we be presented with such a galaxy of stars as we had in the beginning at one and the same time. The best we can hope for is one or maybe two. If we keep this clearly in mind, we will realize that continuing groups at the Hopkins and elsewhere will do well to maintain standards while trying to bring about improvements. Special needs will create special works, and the future will probably see a shining star here and a bulge there, but the general pattern of excellence will belong to no single institution or group.

Chapter 29

WORLD WAR II. HOPKINS POINTS TO COMPLETE FULL TIME

It will be obvious that the years between the wars saw the Hopkins rounding out into a pretty complete and self-contained medical center. Indeed, the Phipps, the School of Hygiene and Public Health, and the Institute of the History of Medicine gave it character and quality far beyond the usual conception of a pure medical center. There was little that patient or doctor couldn't get within its confines. There were laboratories galore, there were dispensaries, wards, and private pavilions, and there was a huge staff bent on the higher things in the field of medicine. If the nation had high regard for the Hopkins, it was not surprising.

Then came World War II, and once again, as it had done a scant twenty-five years before, the Hopkins, like other medical institutions, girded itself for battle. A unit of 1,000 beds was fitted out, staffed, and given the same number (18) as its famous predecessor of World War I, and, oddly enough, its C.O.—Dr. Amos Koontz—was one of the students we took over to France in World War I and graduated there. Like the former unit, its staff was made up for the most part of younger, less important faculty members, numbers of whom had been more active at the Union Memorial and other hospitals of the Secondary Medical Center than at the Hopkins. They had hardly left before the unit was divided into two parts, one becoming No. 18 and the other No. 118. Both were sent to the South Pacific and had distinguished if rather uneventful careers—No. 18 being stationed in the Fiji Islands, No. 118 in Australia. In the Philippine Islands campaign the group from Australia saw more active service at Leyte.

During the absence of so many doctors at war the Medical School and Hospital were manned by the old guard, together with such younger men as were permitted to remain back for the purpose. Some departments were hit harder than others, but they all managed to make out, and when you think that all medical education was accelerated, with classes going on all the year around, it wasn't a bad job that was done. All students except 4-F's and women— who, by the way, were in a rage because they weren't treated like the men—were inducted either into the Army or the Navy and wore the uniform of their respective branches. They were under the command of officers and had certain formations but did not live in barracks or have their studies interfered with. They received governmental remuneration, including tuition, and seemed to be not at all unhappy about it.

I need hardly tell you that the United States, whatever the degree of its actual preparedness in men, planes, and ships at the beginning, was much more onto itself in World War II than in World War I. It had grown up, as it were, in the art of war, and once things got to rolling, men took their stations in orderly fashion and with workmanlike precision. Obviously, civilians predominated and were needed for special work and special knowledge, but this time professionals had better and more know-how, and that was true of the medical as well as other branches of the service. There was no repetition of the Hopkins "episode" in World War II. One even heard rumors that the Army's Medical Department was determined that it shouldn't happen and that it was not by accident that both Hopkins units found themselves stationed in the more quiet zones of the South Pacific. I personally should doubt it, but for the purposes of this story the activities of the Hopkins medical men in this war have not the same significance those of the earlier war had. This only means that they did not become such key figures. (At that, though, the Army's chief medical consultant was Brigadier General Hugh Morgan, one of the third-year men we took over to France with us in World War I and graduated there! He was Professor of Medicine at Vanderbilt University, however, at World War II's outbreak.) Their sacrifice was just as great—even greater, if you consider the time element.*

With the war's end and the return of doctors who had been with the units and numbers who had not, things at the Hopkins resumed

* The history of the Hopkins units of World War II and their accomplishments will doubtless be duly recorded by properly accredited authorities.

their normal course. Students were released from the services, they doffed their uniforms and, perforce, gave up remuneration, including tuition—a blow of real proportions no matter how you looked at it. Accelerated courses also went by the board, and most students and most doctors thought it was a good thing. The staff felt that the man who essays to become a doctor should not be hurried in his studies; he should be given time to think and digest what he has seen and learned. To that I subscribe. I thought I could detect definite signs of strain and tension in men and women and often felt that they needed time off to rest and think—or just do nothing. They were not absorbing the diet of medicine, surgery, pathology, and other things in usual fashion.

There were rumblings among the returned doctor veterans about staff positions and lack of private ward privileges, but they were regarded in the light of the usual gripes of men trying to get used to civilian life and so were pretty much disregarded. When they continued and grew louder it was apparent that something more important was in the air, and in short order it broke. The authorities had decided that the opportune time had arrived to put the full-time system—in abeyance except in top ranks since World War I—into full effect, or as much as they could afford. They had also decided to extend it to other departments not hitherto included.

Inasmuch as most of the men had never been on full time and had been opposed to it from the start—the younger men possibly taking their cue from their older friends—there was general dismay and no little criticism. Especially did the veterans feel that the timing was bad and that scant consideration was being shown their precarious positions. I did not hear one of them mention the word gratitude, but it was plain to be seen that they felt they deserved a better fate from their alma mater. The transition to civilian life after three to five years' military service was bad enough, and the difficulties encountered in rebuilding lost practices were not minimized. They needed hospital privileges badly, but the authorities made it clear that those who had had privileges before would have them curtailed, and those who hadn't had them but had lived in hopes were doomed to disappointment.

This all came out at a staff meeting called for the express purpose of clarification. Dr. Lowell Reed, recently appointed Vicepresident of the University, spoke, and so did Dr. Edwin L. Crosby, newly appointed Director of the Hospital. Both were able, distinguished men who were not responsible for the dictum and both did their best to soften the blow, but I can't say that they succeeded. It wasn't possible. Not only was the Medical School going on full time, but henceforth the full-time men were to set the institution's policy. They had done it only in part before. The audience sat in stunned silence for the most part and then left. A committee of the staff had put certain questions in writing, and Drs. Reed and Crosby had answered them to the best of their ability; they had then signified their willingness to answer any other questions from the floor, but with one or two exceptions none were forthcoming.

I cannot say that I agree with the manner in which the thing was done, nor did I like the timing. The thought even occurs that the men who turned the trick—whoever they were—had not been in the military service and therefore had little firsthand knowledge of the returned veterans' problems. In short, it was a pretty ruthless deal, and it would seem that provisions of some sort could have been made. More than one man remarked that he was utterly sunk, and that all he had looked forward to and hoped for during the long bitter years away from home and country had been knocked into a cocked hat. Other men said it was the usual highhanded way in which the Hopkins did things, and what could you expect? They used you and when they got good and ready cast you off. The general reaction was bad and, so far as I can gather, it has not improved appreciably.

The following letter, which was sent to all staff members, is a good illustration of the Hopkins's methods:

DEAR DOCTOR:

   At the meeting of the Board of Trustees of The Johns Hopkins Hospital which was held today, April 2, 1946, the full-time principle which was adopted at a joint meeting of the Boards of Trustees of the Hospital and University, on October 20, 1913, was reaffirmed unanimously. This was done following a review of the issues as stated in the memorandum "History and Interpretation of the Full-Time Principle."

Pursuant to the Board's instruction I am transmitting to you a copy of this memorandum, which is enclosed. [See appendix.]

EDWIN L. CROSBY, M.D.
Director.

April 2, 1946.

The Board could hardly wait till the boys shed their uniforms!

I mention this and paint the picture because I sympathize deeply with the offended men. They have been given shabby treatment and if the Hopkins has lost some of the respect and loyalty of the group concerned—as undoubtedly it has—it is its own fault. Not only that, it is but another example of a point I have made over and over again in these pages—the utter lack of understanding in high quarters at the Hopkins of social relations and the ways of men. More than any other one thing this is responsible for Baltimore's grudging financial support * and the lip service citizens generally accord the institution. You can't keep pushing people around and taking the high-and-mighty attitude and then expect them to be your friends. Not in this country you can't, and perhaps it wouldn't be a bad idea to have more representatives of the people—including women—on the Hopkins Board of Trustees and fewer lawyers and wealthy men of affairs, who don't know what it's all about.

But while I sound off in righteous indignation I must admit to agreement with the fundamental thesis. I think the time has come when the teachers of medicine and all concerned with it had best give their full time and energies to their duties. Thirty-five years ago I was not of that opinion and, as remarked in a previous chapter, felt that Dr. Welch and the Hopkins had "jumped the gun." Medicine didn't need full time then and wasn't ready. Medicine does need it now and it is ready. The newer advances, the constantly increasing complexities of diagnosis, treatment, care, and prevention

---

* In a recent bid for $3,000,000 locally, hardly more than half was collected. . Yet Baltimore is one of the wealthiest cities in the Union.

of illness, the day-by-day broadening of the entire field—all call urgently for the change. It simply is no longer possible for the teacher of medicine to run in to a medical school and hospital and give a lecture or two, an operative clinic, make ward rounds, and then run out again to attend to his private practice.

It will be less so tomorrow, for the simple reason that the teacher will have to know so much more and have far greater detailed, special knowledge. It will take every minute of his time, every ounce of his energies to keep up with the procession, and even then he will not succeed unless he is relieved of burdensome administrative duties. You may not like it—I admit I don't—but with science on the march in medicine as it is in all other things, we have to forego cherished customs and privileges and condition ourselves to the changing pattern. I used to object to the very idea of full-time men in medicine because, among other things, I thought it stifled competition in the lower echelons of doctors and created a narrow-minded, egotistic, self-centered, dictatorial group in the higher echelons. I thought they'd be constantly knocking off the part-time men on teaching staffs and looking down their noses at lowly private practitioners. And so they would, thirty-five years ago.

They won't now, to much extent, and tomorrow they will do it still less because there will be no part-time teachers in medical schools. All teachers will be on full time—salaried men. And as for private practitioners, they won't have anything to fear either, because they will not be the private practitioners of old—lone eagles who are the darlings of their patients and do the best they can, which isn't always so good if you scrutinize it closely. The practitioner of tomorrow is going to be a member of a group or medical center, or maybe a single hospital, an industrial concern, or a government agency—distributing his knowledge and care and attention in cooperation with other doctors and on a prepayment or other basis that will bring medicine to all people at a price they can afford. In short, this doctor will himself become a full-time man who will work an eight-hour day and get a salary or prorated compensation from his group.

Not everyone will agree with me, but the handwriting is on the wall. Without doubt there will be risks, but when was there a time when we didn't have risks? I certainly can see the doctor who has always worked within a hospital not knowing what the people out-side, more particularly the sick, think and feel; what their reactions are; why they let themselves get into such a fix as they so often do; why they refuse to take advice or to cooperate or even go to a hos-pital for treatment; what price, what fearful price, they pay for ignorance and stupidity; finally, the relation between poverty and illness. I can see how and why he would not know these things, and it makes me shudder to think of this warped institutional man try-ing to tell medical students the facts of life as somewhere along the line they have got to have them explained. The answer is that he mustn't be permitted to try to teach that phase of medicine any more than he would be permitted to teach anything else he knows nothing about. If it is decided that he should teach it, then he should be sent out into the field to learn his subject firsthand. And he could, though it would take time and, to my mind, would be shock-ingly wasteful. A better way, and the way I think will inevitably be followed, will be to have specially trained men with much experi-ence in field work come into the full-time system and do that teach-ing. With the social and economic sides of medicine looming so importantly on the horizon, the time cannot be far distant when we will have full-fledged departments for these subjects and others allied to them in medical schools. When that time comes many of the things we have feared from full-time medical teachers will vanish into thin air.

There remains for discussion the question of remuneration for full-time men, and I have no hesitancy in saying that the success or failure of the system will depend on that. You can't get high-grade men in any walk of life unless you pay them what they think they ought to have. If you pay them less than that, they may take the job, but it will be only until they find something better or until they get all they think they can get out of it, when they will leave. That's been part of the trouble at the Hopkins. In effect, they wanted some-thing for nothing—or very little. In offering men of parts salaries of ten or fifteen thousand dollars when they could make fifty or a hundred, in effect they asked them to do charity. Some would, and some wouldn't. Some could not afford to. That is why, among other things, certain professorships were hawked about, and great embarrassment was created.

The head of a major clinical department at the Hopkins—or any other Grade A medical school—is comparable to the head of a great corporation and should be paid accordingly. The day of playing doctors for suckers is done—or ought to be. Why society should think it abhorrent for the doctor to want real money for his services has never been clear to me—if, indeed, society ever did think that. Why a man of science should be regarded in the light of a wacky critter who knows only test tubes and abstruse problems, a man who never washes his face or has his pants pressed or his hair cut, and wouldn't know what to do with two bits if he ever saw them, has always been a mystery and never was true. He's just like other men and has a wife and children whom he loves and, believe it or not, they, too, need to eat, wear shoes, have a home, have an auto, and go traveling. If they talk more sense and use words the other fellow can't understand, that's the other fellow's tough luck, and he should be the last to say that the scientist is crazy and doesn't need or want money.

In short, if you want men, you've got to pay them. At the moment fifty thousand a year isn't too much for a professor at the Hopkins, and the men under him should be graded and paid accordingly. If medicine hasn't got that kind of money, let medicine go out and get it. Either that or sign off.

Yes, I know all about the men of the scientific departments and the objections they would raise if the lowly clinical men got double or triple their pay, but what of it? It's purely and simply a question of being realistic. What could the average man of science earn if he lost his job—or went out on his own? At that, though, I think they are grossly underpaid.

Chapter 30

THEY'VE GOT YOUTH. WILL HISTORY REPEAT ITSELF? THE NEW AND BIGGER HOPKINS. TOMORROW'S MEDICINE. CONCLUSION

So THE HOPKINS took the bull by the horns, plumped for full time as an all-out policy, and let the chips fall where they might. It won't come about entirely in a day or a week, even a year, but this time it is real. Let no one mistake that.

Some veterans were offered full-time jobs, and some weren't. They couldn't take them all. One man told me that he would like to have accepted but couldn't afford it. Another one that I know did accept, stayed on for a while, and then left for what he considered a better job—in a medical school not on full time. Whether his judgment was good, time alone will tell. In this whole matter the Hopkins didn't take the trouble to explain the reasons for going all out in the new adventure at this particular time, but more than likely they were concerned with the necessity for making new appointments. A flock of them. The Professors of Pathology and Genitourinary Diseases, MacCallum and Hugh Young, had died. The Professors of Medicine and Pediatrics, Longcope and Park, respectively, had reached the age limit and been retired. X ray, long a branch of Surgery, was to be made an independent department. Neurosurgery had lost its chief, Walter Dandy, by death. George Bennett, head of Orthopedics, would shortly retire. Even the Director of the Hospital, Winford Smith, had reached the age limit and been retired. The time was propitious to make the break, and they did it. The reasoning would seem to me to be sound; it is even possible that some explanation was made, but if so, it did not come to my ears. The Departments of Genitourinary Surgery, X ray, Neurosurgery, and Orthopedics had not previously been on full time.

The appointments have now been made, and for my part they are extremely interesting. The Hopkins is reverting to type, or perhaps

210

one might say returning to its earliest days. With the exception of
Arnold Rich in pathology, every man appointed to professorship
at this time is in his early youth—all but one in their thirties. You
will doubtless recall that Welch, Osler, Halsted, and Kelly were
all in their thirties, and the question arises, will history repeat itself? It's a big order, but stranger things have happened. Opinion
among those to whom I have talked is reserved. Few are enthusiastic, but they think it might work out. One man remarked, "This
seems to be the age of youth. They've got youth."

Another commented, "All the men appointed are approximately
the same age. That means that for the next twenty to twenty-five
years all major professorships will be frozen. I don't think that is a
good idea. They don't fire professors at Hopkins, and if one or
maybe two men fail to make good, it's going to be too bad. I'd rather
appoint two or three older men so as to stagger things. It's less of
a gamble."

It is interesting that three of the new men (Rich, Harvey,
Schwentker)—four, if you include Blalock, Professor of Surgery,
aged forty-eight now and appointed some six or seven years ago—
are Hopkins graduates. Richard Te Linde, Professor of Gynecology
since 1939, is also a Hopkins graduate. He is somewhat older than
the new professors, and his department is not yet on full time.
This in itself is a departure, even though, to an extent, involuntary.
One of the chief sources of dissatisfaction among staff members
on down through the years has been the custom of the Hopkins
not to advance its own men of the clinical departments to professorships—not, that is, men who have remained on at the institution. They have appointed the occasional graduate who left
and made his way elsewhere—Longcope and Blalock are examples—but rarely men attached. It has even got so—or had—
that many of the older men urged promising youngsters to take
positions offered by other places if they ever hoped to get recognition at their alma mater. Not all took the advice, but some did,
and from my observations those who didn't ran a bad second.

Once again no explanation ever came from on high, but gossip
had it that they thought men who remained at home became too

ingrown and too set in their ways. They felt that only through outside adventure, field service as it were, and contact with different
schools of thought could a man hope to get the broad view. I think
myself that that attitude has merit, but it should not be permitted
to blind one. There are always exceptions, and rigid rules are bad.
The *modus operandi* as generally understood was to appoint a committee which was to look over the field, consult authorities and make
recommendations. Just how the final choice was made or who had
the final say no one of my acquaintances seemed to know. The only
thing certain was that the respective staffs were not generally called
into conclave and did not make the selections. I am not entirely
certain that that method would have been wise in any case, but in
the one or two instances I know of where staffs took a stand and
sent in a petition, their wishes were not followed. It even came
to be said that any staff man who had the backing of his colleagues
was automatically doomed to disappointment. I wouldn't go that
far, but in one glaring instance where the staff got "all het up" because they were set down, it turned out that the man chosen was
better qualified than their selection and made an outstanding success!

The reason I said appointment of Hopkins's own sons at this
juncture is "to an extent involuntary" is because of the well-known
fact that in certain instances other men were approached first, and
the present incumbent only got the nod when they declined. The
whole success or failure of the gesture is, of course, in the laps of
the gods. As Henry Sigerist said in a conversation I had with him,
"Much will depend on whether the youngsters are overburdened
with executive and administrative duties." He felt that some way
should be found to divest them of all but the most urgent of these.
The modern major department in a big medical institution has
many ramifications and touches other departments. Not every man
has executive ability.

Over and above all this, though, is the question of imponderables
inherent in the medical situation. There has been a vast change since
the days of the Four Saints. Things aren't so simple, and the individual counts for so much less. I feel very hopeful and think the

Hopkins was not only correct but smart to hand things over to young men. More than that, I think all the older men of their respective departments ought to bow out of the picture and let them have their heads—unhampered, unrestricted, uninfluenced by respect, custom, or anything else. It was on the tip of my tongue to say that, even so, they will hardly approach their illustrious predecessors in deeds, in color, in spirit. It isn't in the cards. The possibilities aren't there. But how can one tell and how can one know whether they are there or not? A few short years ago no one thought we'd have such a thing as the atomic bomb with all its inherent possibilities— except maybe Einstein and a scientist or two like him—but here it is. We are told that other things of similar and different nature, all of vast significance, are in the offing. The mind of man roams far afield. I wouldn't put it absolutely past these youths at the Hopkins to approach their predecessors' stature—or even surpass it.

Much, however, will depend on the attitude of the central directorate and their appreciation of things that need to be done—certain of them physical and too long deferred. First and foremost must come adequate dormitories for the students and all that go with them—dining rooms, good kitchens, recreation rooms. The Early Fathers let this little matter ride, probably because the classes were so small as not to make a problem, and probably, too, because they didn't have the money. The result has been that students at the Hopkins have gotten the worst deal imaginable, and only the advent of fraternity houses saved a steadily deteriorating situation—or halfway saved it, since not all men are members. Proper dormitories are a must that admits of no delay.

Another must that should long since have been attended to is a large, first-class hotel that will not only accommodate visitors and relatives and friends of patients but, in addition, will have special accommodations for visiting physicians and facilities for a faculty club. When I tell you that there never has been and isn't now at the Hopkins a place where men of the different schools and departments could gather together informally and get to know each other, you may possibly understand why there has been so little fraternization. Whatever the earlier needs or lack of them, there can be no doubt that for years the greatest single void at the Hopkins has been a decent place near by where people could live and eat and have friendly conversation—even formal meetings. I know of no more helpful thing than friendly acquaintance with men engaged in different pursuits. It is part of the university life and charm for members of different schools and departments to meet and chat about their work, and failure to foster it is a tragic error. Yet that is what they have done at the Hopkins, and I find it difficult to understand or forgive. The medical meetings they have, the historical and other meetings do not solve the problem. When these are over each man goes his own way, and that is that. Since they are held in one or the other of the hospital assembly rooms, there is no place to sit and talk things over afterwards. There should be, and no better place could possibly be found than the rooms of a club—rooms that have easy chairs and lounges with an eating and drinking place at hand.

Nobody knows better than doctors that the best phases of their medical meetings take place in the bars and eating places—sometimes on the golf links—after the formal gatherings—usually in the evenings and often extending into the wee sma' hours. It is then that they take their hair down and exchange ideas and weigh each other's problems and plan for new and bigger and better things over a glass of beer or a·cocktail or so. Why not be honest and realistic? Why not admit, too, that Osler and Welch and Halsted are said to have done just that at Louie Hanselman's place just across the street from Dr. Welch's laboratory? With the exception of the small coterie who belonged to the exclusive Maryland Club, the Hopkins has missed all that in recent years, and to no small degree that accounts for the fact that the men of its different schools and departments are mostly strangers to each other. It also accounts for the fact, well known and often commented on, that visiting doctors, other than the specially invited great lights, get such short shrift and are shown less than scant courtesy. It is of the utmost importance that this matter receive early attention.

The next must is the early erection of apartment houses adjacent to the Hospital for staff men—young and old, single as well as married. And when I say apartment houses I include everything that goes with them that makes for good and comfortable living—centers for purchasing food, household, and other goods; garages; even movies. In short, the Hopkins Medical Center is a huge undertaking today and will be vast tomorrow. It should be regarded in that light, and men with the vision to see all sides and phases of it must take over. The hotel that I talk of should have a great assembly room for the general meetings that now take place in the Hospital. There should also be anterooms for smaller gatherings, dining halls, cafeterias, bars—all things calculated to attract men and hold them. If you are going to have a big, growing, vibrant organization, you've got to have all the things that go with it. The Hopkins authorities have been singularly slow to see that and completely unwilling to do the obvious. It goes without saying that ways and means will have to be found to place the apartments mentioned above within the means of those who are to occupy them.

Finally, there remains for discussion the Hospital itself. The present plant has become outmoded for the most part and is gradually being rebuilt. There was some talk of moving it out to the country near by—in part if not *in toto*—but apparently that has been given up. I personally am glad. I think the Hospital—laboratories and all—should stay right where it is, but I do not think it should be rebuilt along the old lines—pavilion system with buildings six or seven stories high. The place has outgrown that; it has become too big; you can't have departments too segregated or too far from each other—or shouldn't. Better go up high in the air like other places —with departments on different floors, and escalators and elevators, general and special, carrying you to them. It saves time and exertion, and more fraternization is possible between departments and staff—more general interest. Nobody has asked my opinion, but if it were left to me, I'd scrap the main building on Broadway first— it's a terrible firetrap anyhow—and erect in its stead a huge structure of massive proportions, going high in the air—thirty to forty stories—and with that as a nucleus build the rest of the Hospital around it and in proportion. To do that I'd call in architects and engineers who would promulgate the master plan, but the underlying

idea would emanate from the doctors. It might be that the club suggested could be specially built in the very middle of the quadrangle,
where it would be readily available to all staffs. And just to prove
how utilitarian I am, I would have a huge underground garage
built under the main hospital building and extending back under the
club. I'd also provide landing space for helicopters on the roof!

These are the physical quantities—the dormitories, hotels, eating
houses, clubs, hospital buildings—and in the nature of things they
are the easiest to supply. Vast sums of money will be required to
encompass them, but when was there a time when doctors couldn't
command money if they showed the need? What if the times are
changing and great private philanthropists with their vast fortunes
are fast disappearing? Let the doctors change, too, and plumb other
sources—even if that means the government. I grow impatient with
the order of medical mind that prefers to remain static and sees
ulterior motives in every move made by officials whose duty it is to
safeguard the people of this nation. Rather let the doctors develop
a statesmanship of their own that will permit them to take the
broad viewpoint and thus direct their own destinies and those of
their charges. Let the Hopkins lead!

Nor do I see difficulties with the things of the mind—meaning
science. Looked at factually, the march of science is irresistible. It
manufactures its own motivating force or, if not that, has it all
ready and at hand in man's insatiable, innate, unconscious, uncon-
trollable urge to investigate the obscure and the unknown. You see
it on every hand, in all walks of life, and the only difficulty comes
in harnessing it or utilizing it to the best advantage. Unfortunately,
it cannot always be timed to our needs, and unfortunately, too, there
are bulges in one direction, indentations in another. Yet the over-all
advance continues, and if society can learn to coordinate its activities better and bring the forces of its mind to bear on urgent needs,
the line could be straightened out. I refer to the great strides recently made in dealing with infectious processes in comparison to
the continued stalemate in dealing with cancer.

Medical men have clung too tenaciously to their individual free-
doms for their own and the people's good. They can't see that by

reason of the very advances made in science the day of the individual is done, and from now on it will be groups, teams, which will create. Do you think we could have had spectacular success in war by any other means, and doesn't it follow that the reason doctors haven't progressed with cancer and colds and things of like nature is because these diseases are of such complex nature as to demand newer organized, coordinated attack? I think this is on the way now, and before long you will see tangible results. So when I say that the things of the mind give me little concern you will understand that I visualize enormous scientific advance, whether provision is made for it or not, and quite regardless of needs, desires, wars, peace, struggles, communism, democracy, atomic bombs, or anything else. I liken science to the sexual urge. It is overpowering; it is innate in the human being; nothing can stop it; the only concern we need have is controlling it.

I lay greater stress on the things of the soul—and I use this term for want of a better one—the intangibles of life, the spiritual values, the things that require understanding and thought and have no connection with an urge or irresistible force. It is not my purpose to write a thesis on the subject, but when one compares the high position of scientific accomplishment with the lowly position of social and economic progress it is not only appalling but downright discouraging. I think the medical profession has much to answer for but it is not exclusively to blame. It makes no sense to me that we have all these wonderful things about us that could and should make life better and easier and more worth while, yet withal there is more misery now than ever and greater dissatisfaction. We have constant wars, and the killing gets bigger and better. With the greatest of all wars barely ended, men who were allies cannot now agree on a way of life that will make for peace and good living and quiet and rest. I say it is a matter chiefly of the soul, and that man needs badly to understand the meaning of things. Especially is this true of the doctors, who could do so much more good if they were of a different mind and, realizing that civilization is in a period of transition, lead the way in the newer approach. Better than anyone else they know that poverty and disease go hand in hand, yet all they do is get out bigger and better operations and sure-fire cures for disease in full swing. You hear little talk of prevention. Prevention is not so spectacular. They teach their men and women to be doctors, but teach little of the meaning of doctoring. They cling to the past in custom and view the future only in terms of science. They turn a deaf ear to pleadings for different methods of distributing their knowledge to the masses, and each day we see the cost of being sick rising to prohibitive heights. World affairs, trends in which they have as big a stake as any other group, leave them cold. Instead of becoming the force for good they could be, they stand aloof, and men of lesser attainments make weighty decisions they are not always competent to make—and formulate plans—some of them profoundly affecting the medical profession.

It is an understatement to say that the Hopkins was more colorful and romantic in its earlier years. That was the era of color and romance in our nation, and an elusive but nonetheless definite pattern was being unfolded. Fabulous men of rugged character, few inhibitions, and great daring were everywhere molding it. The Hopkins was part and parcel of the whole—pioneer in its field even as the House of Morgan, that of the Rockefellers, the Edisons, Goulds, Harrisons, Fords, and others were pioneers in theirs. Great dynasties were created, and that at the Hopkins was not the least of them— nor was its enveloping aura the only one cast.

Generally speaking, the Hopkins has been a happy institution— happier at some times than others, like people. At the moment, what with structural changes being effected and world-wide unrest and uncertainty, it is in one of its less happy periods. As for luck, I think it has had more than its share. I only hope its luck holds.

One thing I feel should be stressed. Perhaps I should have pounded it more, but I took for granted that it was generally known and understood. Hopkins men have been free. True, the directorate ruled firmly and brooked no interference and rarely gave explanation of its actions, but it never told a man what he should think or do or say, how he should act or teach—or anything else. There wasn't obnoxious prejudice, either—religious or racial. From time to time you heard rumblings, but they never were seriously regarded by anyone. So far as I personally know the admission of Negroes to the Medical School never came up authoritatively. There wouldn't have been much point to it since few would have been able to qualify—up to the present time. Surely they will be admitted in the not too distant future. Why shouldn't they?

Without freedom there could have been little happiness at the Hopkins, and certainly there wouldn't have been the spirit and high morale that are the mark of the institution. I don't know exactly what luck is, of course, but whatever its nature those who are happiest and most successful seem to have it in greatest measure. I suppose it's partly timing and the willingness to let your imagination run when things are going your way. The man who is playing on "velvet" can afford to gamble, though heaven forbid that I should say the Hopkins ever gambled—even though at times it did, and heavily—and most often won!

There was always imagination at the Hopkins and the spirit of adventure—both more in evidence early than late because of increasing age and solidity of the directorate. This is a natural sequence, but somehow, some way, they seem to be overcoming it. I can see the appointment of so many young men to key positions only in that light. It would appear that they have decided once again to let their imaginations run, and I, for one, think they are dead right.

A few years hence we surely will see cancer controlled or entirely overcome, and the same will be true of the common cold, perhaps the most evil of all human scourges. We shall have chemicals of more wondrous nature and effectiveness than even penicillin, and tuberculosis, venereal disease, and other affections will fade out of the picture. Poverty and the ravages of old age, preventive medicine, problems of the mind, metabolism, and developmental things will then occupy importantly men of medicine. To cope with them they will have to be educated along broader and different lines. It won't be sufficient to know only diseased processes or to be able to do tests, make diagnoses, carry out operations. Doctors will have to know people and their ways and problems; they will have to develop a statesmanship that will enable them to take their place among the world's leaders.

In short, I view tomorrow's medicine as the greatest of all adventures doctors have yet taken and I firmly believe they will bring comfort and health and the better life to people in greater measure than ever before. But it will take courage and imagination and strength and work—also freedom. That's why I like this recent gesture of the Hopkins directorate. They see the world of tomorrow in terms of youth—and I have no doubt that Welch, Osler, Halsted, and Kelly would applaud them if they were here.

Appendix

HISTORY AND INTERPRETATION OF THE
FULL-TIME PRINCIPLE

(OFFICIAL)

IN OCTOBER, 1913, under the leadership of Dr. Welch, who in addition
to his Medical School duties was then Chairman of the Administrative
Committee of the University, the full-time principle was fully explored
and established. The Trustees of both Hospital and University at a joint
meeting approved the principle of the reorganization of the departments
of Medicine, Surgery, and Pediatrics that was required to put the plan
into effect. The Medical Faculty had already given its unanimous ap-
proval.* It was by general consent, therefore, that the plan was adopted
and that funds were sought to support it. The generous response of the
General Education Board to an appeal for funds gave the necessary
financial stability.

For the thirty-three year period in which the full-time plan has been
in operation the effects which were anticipated have been realized. The
plan was extended to the Department of Obstetrics in 1919, of Psychiatry in 1923, of Ophthalmology in 1925, and to appointments in
Urology in 1945.

To finance on a full-time basis those departments that do not have
adequate supporting endowments it is necessary to apply the fees from
private patients to the general support of the departments concerned.
Such application was in view in October, 1913, when the full-time
principle was established. "Exhibit 1," as it was called, which Dr.
Welch was to use at his discretion in approaching the General Education
Board contains this significant sentence: "They (members of the full-
time staff) would be free to render any service required by humanity
or science, but from it they would be expected to derive no pecuniary
benefit. Fees charged by the Hospital for professional service to private
patients, within or without the Hospital, by members of the full-time
staff, such as at present are paid directly to the physician, would be
used to promote the objects for the attainment of which this request (for
funds from the General Education Board) is made." The same exhibit
goes on to say, "in the Dispensary, in clinical teaching, and in the
teaching of special topics, men engaged partly in practice can be ad-
vantageously used to some extent." What Dr. Welch called "scientific
medicine" determined the conditions upon which the Trustees and the

* As noted this was not entirely correct.

221

Medical Faculty had agreed. Out of the devotion of the full-time men and the application of their entire time to the advancement of clinical medicine it was sought to strengthen and advance medical education and research. It was this action and the reduction of numbers in the School (which could be undertaken because of additional endowment) that were expected further to raise the standard of the School that had already taken so high a position when founded in 1893 on a post-graduate basis.

At this time it is desired to refer to the "advantageous use" in the building of the Medical School of the part-time men who were designated in Dr. Welch's report as "men engaged partly in practice." It has been the good fortune of the School of Medicine to be located in a city that has grown from a half-million to a million in population. This has permitted and encouraged men of ability, many of them trained in the Hopkins School of Medicine, to establish themselves here and to add their abilities to those of the full-time staff in the conduct of the teaching and research for which the School has become famous. We have valued the services of these men. We have given them appointments in the School, drawn upon them for time and knowledge in the clinical developments of the Hospital, and treated them as members of the family. The benefits have been reciprocal. The men engaged "partly in practice" have enjoyed hospital privileges. In their beginning years they have benefited from the experiences of the dispensary. They have formed attractive associations with men of high calibre and stimulating personalities. We have never doubted the policy or wavered in the practice of associating eminent clinicians with the School of Medicine. We shall continue the practice in the years to come. There is nothing in the policy of the University or the Hospital that will in any way affect the integrity of the principle of association of these men with the full-time men in the continued strengthening of a great School and Hospital.

It should be clear, however, that the responsibility for the policies that have been adopted lie with the Medical Faculty and the Trustees. They must evaluate the system under which we work and recommend and authorize any changes in it. During the past thirty-three years they have steadily supported the full-time principle and extended it. Such extension has not eliminated part-time men. In specific instances it may have restricted their use of hospital facilities. The growth of the city itself required an expansion of hospital services far beyond any that were contemplated in 1867 when Johns Hopkins wrote his will, or in 1889 when the Johns Hopkins Hospital was opened. In addition, the number of physicians and surgeons in proportion to the population has increased. All this has been a part of a general rise in the standard of living. This means that the facilities of the Johns Hopkins Hospital were never adequate for the purposes of either the full-time men or all those part-time men who were connected with the University's School of Medicine. While the Hospital has grown, its growth has not been rapid enough to accommodate all the demands upon its facilities by all those who held appointments on the staff.

In extending the full-time system to departments in which there is insufficient endowment income, we are obliged to fall back upon fees and to use them in the meaning proposed in 1913 by applying them to the objects of the full-time plan, namely the improvement of teaching and the advancement of "scientific medicine." It is not proposed to exclude part-time men, and on the other hand it is not proposed to abandon the full-time principle. The purpose of the present discussion of the full-time principle and its reaffirmation is to clear up any doubt as to the position of the Hospital and the University on this matter, while assuring the part-time men engaged in private practice that we intend to deal with them fairly and on a reciprocal basis while leaving the determination of policy in the hands of those who have public responsibility for it, namely the Trustees of the University and Hospital and the corresponding administrative officers.

April 1, 1946

BIBLIOGRAPHY

I acknowledge with gratitude especial aid from the following books:

BUCKLER, W. H.: *Assembling the Homewood Site,* Johns Hopkins Press, 1941.

CHESNEY, ALAN M.: *The Flowering of an Idea,* Johns Hopkins Press, Baltimore, 1939.

CHESNEY, ALAN M.: *The Johns Hopkins Hospital and the Johns Hopkins School of Medicine: A Chronicle,* Vol I, *Early Years. 1867–1893,* Johns Hopkins Press, Baltimore, 1943. (The second volume remains to be written.)

CLAPSATTLE, HELEN: *The Doctors Mayo,* Garden City Publishing Company, Inc., Garden City, New York, 1943.

CULLEN, THOMAS S.: *Early Medicine in Maryland* (Privately printed).

CULLEN, THOMAS S.: *Henry Mills Hurd. The First Superintendent of the Johns Hopkins Hospital,* Johns Hopkins Press, Baltimore, 1920.

CULLEN, THOMAS S.: "Max Brödel, 1870–1941. Director of the First Development of Art as Applied to Medicine in the World," *Bulletin of the Medical Library Association,* 33, 5–29, 1945.

CUSHING, HARVEY: *Consecratio Medici and Other Papers,* Little, Brown & Company, Boston, 1928.

CUSHING, HARVEY: *The Life of Sir William Osler,* Oxford University Press, 1925.

FINNEY, JOHN M. T.: *A Surgeon's Life,* G. P. Putnam's Sons, New York, 1940.

FLEXNER, ABRAHAM: *Daniel Coit Gilman: Creator of the American Type of University,* Harcourt, Brace & Company, Inc., New York, 1947.

FLEXNER, SIMON, and JAMES THOMAS FLEXNER: *William Henry Welch and the Heroic Age of American Medicine,* The Viking Press, Inc., New York, 1941.

FREEMAN, ALLEN W.: *Five Million Patients,* Charles Scribner's Sons, New York, 1946.

FRENCH, JOHN C.: *A History of the University Founded by Johns Hopkins,* Johns Hopkins Press, Baltimore, 1946.

FULTON, JOHN F.: *Harvey Cushing: A Biography,* Charles C. Thomas, Publisher, Springfield, Ill., 1946.

HALSTED, WM. STEWART: "The Employment of Fine Silk in Preference to Catgut. The Advantages of Transfixing Tissues and Vessels in Controlling Haemorrhage. Also an Account of the Introduction of Gloves, Gutta-percha Tissue and Silver Foil," the Welch Bibliophilic Society, 1939.

"Harvey Cushing's Seventieth Birthday Party, April 8, 1939. Speeches, Letters and Tributes," published for the Harvey Cushing Society, Charles C. Thomas, Publisher, Springfield, Ill., 1919.

"The History of Base Hospital No. 18, A.E.F. [Johns Hopkins Unit]," published privately by Base Hospital No. 18 Association, 1919.

LAMSON, PAUL D.: "John Jacob Abel," *Bulletin of the Johns Hopkins Hospital,* vol. 68, 119–158, 1941.

LONG, PERRIN H., and ELEANOR A. BLISS: *The Clinical and Experimental Use of Sulphanilamide and Sulphapyridine and Allied Compounds,* The Macmillan Company, New York, 1939.

McCALLUM, W. G.: *William Stewart Halsted: Surgeon,* Johns Hopkins Press, Baltimore, 1930.

NYBURG, SIDNEY L.: *The Buried Rose: Legends of Old Baltimore,* Alfred A. Knopf, Inc., 1932.

OSLER, WILLIAM: *Aequanimitas and Other Addresses,* P. Blakiston's Son & Co., Philadelphia, 1904.

OSLER, WILLIAM: *Science and Immortality,* Houghton Mifflin Company, Boston, 1904.

SIGERIST, HENRY E.: *The University at the Crossroads,* Henry Schuman, Inc., New York, 1946.

SLAUGHTER, FRANK G.: *The New Science of Surgery,* Julian Messner, Inc., Publishers, New York, 1946.

THOM, HELEN HOPKINS: *A Silhouette,* Johns Hopkins Press, Baltimore, 1929.

YOUNG, HUGH: *A Surgeon's Autobiography,* Harcourt, Brace & Company, Inc., New York, 1940.

INDEX

A

Abel, John J., 14, 16, 32, 53–54, 60–64, 66–69, 71, 95, 137, 193
Acromegaly, 87
Adrenalin, 60–61
Alumni, 57
American College of Surgeons, 154–155
American Medical Association, 187
Ames, Joe, 15
Anatomical Institute of Leipzig, 131
Anatomy, 14, 32, 34, 53–59, 80, 137
  quiz compendium on, 58–59
Anesthesia, cocaine, 11–12
  local, 63
Anesthetists, 51
Aneurisms, 20, 96, 136
Animal experimentation, 91–96, 108
  (See also Surgery, animal)
Ann Arbor, Michigan, 62
Anticoagulants, 68n.
Antitoxin, 92
Antivivisectionists, 88–89, 94
Argonne Forest Battle, 166
Art, applied to medicine, 23–24, 131–134
Artificial kidney, 66, 68
Atkinson, I. E., 35
Austrian, Charles R., 143
Autopsies, 72–73

B

Bacteriology, 30, 80, 113, 123, 163
Baer, William, 51, 143, 167
Baetjer, Frederick H. (Harry), 51–52, 128-130
Baltimore, 2–4, 10–11, 15, 24, 49–51, 66, 68, 87, 124–125, 133, 135, 138–139, 194, 206
  alumni meetings at, 57
  City Health Department, 120
  description of, 26–27, 86

Baltimore, Secondary Medical Center in, 142, 145, 147–151, 202
  (See also University of Maryland)
Baltimore fire, 28, 82
Baltimore and Ohio Railroad, 4, 14, 31
Baltimore Orioles, 15–16
Banting, Frederick Grant, 62
Barker, Lewellys F., 79–81, 84, 139, 163–164, 185–186
Base Hospital No. 18, A.E.F., 165–169
  in World War II, 202
  No. 118, 202
Baseball, 15, 187
Bean, Robert Bennett, 55
Becker, Herman, 131n.
Beers, Clifford, 102
Bellevue Hospital Medical College, 11
Bennett, George, 210
Bernheim, Bertram M., 181n.
  anecdotes about, 15, 24–25, 55, 59, 64–69, 89–90, 93–94, 104, 115–117, 125–126, 130, 157–158, 160–162, 196–199
Bethesda, Maryland, government's medical center at, 66
Bichloride poisoning, 66
Big Four, 36, 76
  (See also Halsted; Kelly; Osler; Welch)
Billings, John Shaw, 9–10, 14, 29
Biophysics, 120–121, 163
Biostatistics, 118n.
Blackfan, Kenneth, 100
Blalock, Alfred, 108, 112, 184, 211
Bleeding, control of, 21
Bliss, Eleanor, 193
Blood, coagulation of, 65
  research on, 60
Blood clots, 65, 67
Blood transfusion, 64–69, 95–96, 148, 158
  sodium citrate in, 68, 169
  in World War II, 168–169

Bloodgood, Joseph, 24–25, 50, 71, 86, 132, 143–145, 149–150, 156, 163, 178n.
"Blue baby operation," 108, 184
Boggs, Tom, 50, 71, 143, 167
Boston, 50, 82
Brady, James Buchanan (Diamond Jim), 111, 114, 146
Brady Urological Institute, 111–117
Brain tumors, 87, 97, 100
Braune, W., 131
Breslau, 10
British College of Surgeons, 154
Brödel, Max, 23, 131–134
Brown, James, 51
Brown, Tom, 143
Brunton, Sir Thomas Lauder, 12
Bryn Mawr College, 32
Burnam, Curtis, 23

C

Cancer, 21, 23, 216, 219
  of the breast, 158
  from X ray, 130
Carrel, Alexis, 24
Chemistry, 38, 80
  physiological, 163
Chesnay, Alan M., 80n.
Chew, Samuel C., 35
Chicago, 154–155, 187–188
  medical center in, 138
"Chief" (see Osler, William)
Church Home and Infirmary, 144, 150
Civil War, 2, 26–27
Clifton (Hopkins estate), 27–29
Clinical-Pathological Conference, 72–74
Clinics, 38, 40, 80, 136, 190
  diagnostic, 57–58
  eye, 170–171
  Dr. Halsted's, 86
  operative, 153
  Dr. Osler's, 73
  pediatric, 107–110
  purpose of, 192
Cocaine, 11–12, 22
Cocaine anesthesia, 11–12

Cohnheim, J. F., 10
Cole, Rufus, 80
College of Physicians and Surgeons of New York, 35
Columbia University, 7, 138, 185
Coronary thrombosis, 100
Councilman, William Thomas, 14, 48
C.P.C. (see Clinical-Pathological Conference)
Crosby, Edwin L., 205–206
Crowe, Sam, 51
Cullen, Thomas S., 23, 50, 133, 143–145, 149–150, 163
Cushing, Harvey, 50, 64, 71, 82–83, 85–99, 112, 131–132, 139, 143, 146–148, 156, 163, 174–175, 184, 186, 191, 193

D

Dandy, Walter, 97, 99–101, 184, 191, 210
Dartmouth, 35n.
Davis, Staige, 97
Deafness, 97
Deaver, John, 21
Débridement operation, 116, 165–166
Dicumarol, 68n.
Diphtheria, 92
Dispensaries, 29, 34, 38–40, 74–75, 109–110, 202
  pediatric, 109
  surgical, 113, 153
  for tuberculosis, 82
Dissecting rooms, 54–56
Dogs, dissecting of, 24–25
  experiments on, 55, 64, 66–67, 95–96
    (See also Animal experimentation; Surgery, animal)
Drugs, 60, 163, 193
  (See also names of drugs)

E

Eastman, Nicholas J., 127
Edinburgh, 76
England, scientific medicine in, 53

Epidemiology, 118n.–119
Epinephrine, 60–62
Eye diseases, 170–171
Examinations, in anatomy, 55, 57
  fourth-year, 157–158
  of patients, 19–20, 33, 71, 135

F

Fairley, Brig. N. Hamilton, 193n.
Finney, John M. T., 41, 50, 65, 88,
  95, 112–113, 139, 143–145, 149–
  150, 153–164, 166–167, 169, 185,
  190
Firor, Warfield M., 100
Fisher, William A., 143, 159, 162, 166
Flexner, Abraham, 9n., 14–15, 102n.,
  173–174
Flexner, James Thomas, 175n.
Flexner, Simon, 48, 71, 102n., 131,
  175n.
4-F's, 203
Four F's of typhoid fever, 20, 136
Four Galloping Horsemen, 14, 16
  (See also Halsted; Kelly; Os-
  ler; Welch)
Four Great Doctors, 43
  (See also Halsted; Kelly; Osler;
  Welch)
Four Physicians," "The (painting),
  7, 183
Four Saints," "The, 7, 146, 212
  description of, 8–9
  teamwork of, 13
  (See also Halsted; Kelly; Osler;
  Welch)
France, 164–168, 188, 202
  scientific medicine in, 53
Freeman, Allen W., 119
French, John C., 5
Friedenwald, Jonas, 171
Friends (see Society of Friends)
Frost, W. H., 119
Full-time principle, 163–164, 204–210
  history and interpretation of, 221–
  223
Fulton, John F., 83, 85–86, 89n., 186n.
Futcher, Thomas B., 50, 83, 143, 163

G

Gangrene, 25
Garrett, Mary Elizabeth, 30–31
Garrett, Robert W., 31
Garrison, Fielding, 175
Gatch, Willis, 51
Gatch bed, 51
Geiling, E. M. K., 66
General practitioners, women as, 34
Genitourinary diseases, 32, 51, 113
  male, 111
Genitourinary surgery (see Surgery)
Geraghty, John Timothy, 113
Germany, 62
  scientific medicine in, 53–54
Gigantism, 87, 97
Gildersleeve, Basil L., 1, 15, 32
Gilman, Daniel C., 1, 9–11, 14–15, 29,
  31
Glasgow, 13
Goiter, 96
G.O.M. (see Morphine)
Goodnow, Frank J., 172
Goodyear Rubber Company, 177
Graduate education, in American
  medicine, 1, 36, 192–200
  in nursing, 179
Gray's Anatomy, 55
Gwynn, Mary, 30
Gynecology, 13, 23, 52, 122, 163, 211

H

Halsted, William S. ("Professor"), 1,
  7–8, 13–14, 16, 36, 39, 50–51, 54,
  57–58, 69, 85–87, 89, 94, 96–97,
  108, 111–112, 128–129, 136–137,
  146, 148, 153, 155–158, 163, 185,
  187, 189, 193, 211–214, 220
  and cocaine, 11–12, 22
  death of, 184
  description of, 20–22
  and rubber gloves, 177–178
Halsted, Mrs., 156, 178
Hamburger, L. P., 143
Hamman, Louis, 143
Hampton, Caroline, 177–178
  (See also Halsted, Mrs.)

Hanselman, Louis, 16, 214
Harkness, Edward S., 172
Harriet Lane Home for Invalid Children, 107–110
Harvard, 16, 48–49, 85, 97–98, 138, 175
  Public Health and Hygiene Departments, 118–119
Harvey, William, 211
Health officers, need for, 119
Heart disease, 136
  congenital, 184
  (*See also* "Blue baby operation"; Coronary thrombosis)
Hebrew Aged Home, 144, 149
Heparin, 68n.
Hirudin, 66–68
His, Wilhelm, 131
Homewood, 28
Hookworm disease, 118
Hoover, Herbert, 175
Hopkins, Elizabeth (cousin of Johns), 3, 5–6
Hopkins, Gerard (uncle of Johns), 3
Hopkins, Hannah (mother of Johns), 2–3
Hopkins, Johns, 1–6
  Baltimore's opinion of, 4–5, 27
Hopkins, Joseph (nephew of Johns), 4
Hopkins, Samuel (father of Johns), 2
  children of, 2–3
Hopkins Brothers, 3
Hopkins Unit, in World War I, 163–168
  in World War II, 202–203
Hormones, 61–62
Horn, August, 131n.
Hospital School for Crippled Children, 51
Hospital for the Women of Maryland, 144, 150
Howard, William T., 35
Howell, William H., 16, 53–54, 60, 64, 68–69, 71, 118, 137, 200
Howland, John, 107

Hughson, Walter, 97
Hunner, Guy L., 50, 143
Hunter, John, 89
Hunterian Laboratory for Experimental Medicine and Surgery, 24, 88–89, 91–94, 97, 99, 147–148, 160, 187
Hurd, Henry M., 11
Hydrocephalus, pathogenesis of, 100
Hygiene, and public health, 81
Hypophysis, 97

I

Illustrations, anatomical, 23–24, 131–134
Insulin, 62
Interns, 18–19, 43, 113, 125–126, 178

J

Jacobs, Henry Barton, 83
Janeway, Theodore C., 185
Jefferson Medical School, 50
Jenkins, Mrs. May McShane, 120–121
Johns Hopkins Historical Society, 70, 72
Johns Hopkins Hospital Bulletin, 70, 72
Johns Hopkins Medical Society, 70–72
Johns Hopkins University, 4–5, 7, 9, 15–16
  architecture of, 28
  Board of Directors, 9, 12, 27, 30–32, 206, 221–223
  fame of, 13–14, 138, 146
  first location of, 27–28
  Graduate School, 9, 11, 138
  Medical School and Hospital, alumni of, 57
  appointment to staff of, 211–212
  atmosphere of, 136
  and Baltimore fire, 28, 82
  between wars, 183–192, 200–201
  Board of Consulting Physicians, 35

Johns Hopkins University, Medical School and Hospital, Brady Urological Institute, 111–117
coeducation at, 30–34
  and marriage, 33–34
compared with Mayo Clinic, 139–141
  with other hospitals, 46–47
curriculum of, 37–39
dental instruction at, 157
departmental system of, 47–50
departments and clinics of, chemical, 53
  genitourinary surgery, 51, 210
  gynecology 52
  hygiene, 65
  medicine, 10, 76, 221
  neurosurgery, 210
  nose and throat, 51
  obstetrics, 221
  orthopedics, 51
  outpatient, 74
    in obstetrics, 123–126
  pathology, 52
  pediatrics, 107–110, 221
  pharmacology, 60
  physiology, 60
  psychiatry, 221
    (See also Phipps Psychiatric Clinic)
  scientific, 53
  social service, 74–75
  surgery, 12, 221
  X ray, 51
dispensary (see Dispensaries)
Faculty and staff of, 31–32, 70–74, 221–222
five distinctive features of, 70–75
full-time system at, 163–164, 204–210, 221–223
housing facilities at, 30, 213
laboratories at, 38, 46, 48, 80, 142, 147–148
  Dr. Abel's, 63
  Dr. Howell's, 64
  Dr. Welch's, 11, 29, 48, 54, 122
  for eye diseases, 170

Johns Hopkins University, Medical School and Hospital (See also Hunterian Laboratory)
lack of privileges at, 148–152
location of, 28–29
medical graduates of, 192–201
  compared with others, 195–200
medical students of, 103–104
Negroes at, 219
nursing school, 33, 177
  graduate, 179
opening of, 32, 37, 39
and outside practice, 142–145, 163–164, 204–209
pavilion system at, 29, 37, 202, 215
planning and development of, 1, 8–14
policy toward clinicians, 142–152, 163–164, 185, 190
present needs of, intangible, 217–218
  physical, 213–216
reasons for greatness of, 112
research at, 37, 60–69, 80, 85–98, 100–101, 108, 111–114, 118–121, 123, 128–130, 147–148, 193
resident system at, 43–52
salaries at, 142–143
School of Art as Related to Medicine, 134
School of Hygiene and Public Health, 81, 118–121, 172, 202
  Department of Biophysics, 120
as Supreme Court of American medicine, 138–139
tenure of office at, 189–190
and University of Maryland, 35–36
Welch Institute for the History of Medicine, 151, 172–176, 191, 202
Wilmer Institute for Diseases of the Eye, 170–171, 191
women on staff of, 33
Women's Memorial Fund, 30–32
in World War I, 163–168
in World War II, 202–203

Johns Hopkins University, Philosophical Faculty, 9
  present site of, 28
Johnston, Christopher, 35
Jones, Walter, 54
Journal of Experimental Medicine, founding of, 61
Journal of Pharmacology and Experimental Therapeutics, founding of, 61

K

Kamphaus, Charlie, 63
Kelly, Howard A., 11, 13–14, 16, 18, 21–25, 31, 36, 50, 52, 69, 112, 122, 129, 131, 137, 139, 163, 193, 200, 211, 220
  description of, 7–8
  private hospital of, 23, 146
Keyser, William, 28
Kidneys, 111, 113
King, Elizabeth, 30
Kleb, Arnold C., 173
Koontz, Amos, 202

L

Lacrosse team, 128, 130
Lamson, Paul D., 63
"Latchkeyers," 82–83
Latimer, T. S., 35
Leipzig, 10, 23, 172
  Anatomical Institute of, 131
  Physiological Institute of, 131
Leukemia, 95
Lewis, Dean, 57–59, 185–190
Lewisohn, Richard, 68
London, 12
Long, Perrin, 193
Longcope, Warfield, 185–188, 210–211
Louis Hanselman's place, 16, 214
Ludwig, Carl, 10, 131

M

MacCallum, William George, 71–72, 97, 120, 210
McCrae, Thomas, 50, 83
Macewen, Sir William, 13

McGill University, 7
Magendie, François, 88
Malarial fever, 135
Mall, Franklin P., 14, 16, 32, 53–57, 59–60, 71, 84, 131, 137
Marshall, Ken, 193
Martin, Franklin, 62, 154–155
Maryland Club, 214
Maryland State Board of Health, 118
Massachusetts General, 50, 85–86
Mayo, Charles, 140
Mayo, William C., 140
Mayo, William W., 140
Mayo Clinic, 66, 133, 139–141, 184, 192
Medical education, 11
  for women, 30–34
  (*See also* Graduate education)
Medical history, 172–176
Medical schools, number of, 137
Medicine, 11–12, 14, 30, 53, 163, 210
  American, 1, 8, 48, 80, 138, 147
  clinical, 53
  cooperation in, 184
  discoveries in, right to use, 149
  future of, 219–220
  preventive, 219
  residents in, 44, 46–49
  scientific, 62–63, 107
    women in, 34
  social, 160, 208
  teaching of, 206–209, 219
    remuneration for, 208–209
  women in, 32–34
Medicine at the Crossroads, 160
Mental ills, 102–106
Mercy Hospital, 145
Metchnikoff, Élie, 17
Meyer, Adolph, 103, 105
Moore, Earl, 143
Morgan, Brig. Gen. Hugh, 203
Morphine, 20, 162
Murphy, John B., 138

N

Nerves, suture of, 57
Neurology, 87, 191

New York City, 7, 11, 68, 185
Nobel Prize, 97
Nurses, 18–19, 125–126
  administrative, 179–181
  and marriage, 178–179
  and rubber gloves, 177
  shortage of, 180–182
  standards for, 182
Nutrition, 120

O

Obstetrics, 11, 36, 52, 122–127, 163
  Williams's textbook on, 123
Old Ben, 18
Operations (see Surgery; names of operations)
Ophthalmology, 221
Opie, Eugene L., 71–72
Orthopedics, 51, 87, 210
Osler, Revere, 8, 79
Osler, William ("Chief"), 1, 7–8, 11–14, 16, 18–20, 31, 36, 39, 49, 58, 62, 69–73, 80–83, 87, 112, 129, 131, 136–137, 139, 146, 163, 172, 186, 200, 211, 214, 220
  death of, 79
  farewell address of, 77–79
  resignation of, 76–77
  return visits of, 79
  Saturday nights with, 40–42
Osler, Mrs., 40–41, 76, 79, 83
Osmosis, 67
Oxford University, 76, 83

P

Pancoast, Omar, 143, 158
Park, Edwards A., 107–108, 210
Pathology, 9–10, 12, 18, 38, 48, 52, 58, 80, 122–123, 210–211
Patients, 19, 23, 38–39
  consideration for, 135
  examination of, 19–20, 33, 71, 135
Peabody, George, 5
Pearl, Raymond, 119
Pediatrics, 107–110, 163, 210
  women in, 34

Penicillin, 95, 169, 194
"Perineal prostatectomy," 111
Peripheral vascular diseases, 151
Pershing, Gen. John, 114–115
Pharmacology, 14, 32, 38, 53, 64, 138
Phenolsulphonephthalein, 113
Philadelphia, 30, 50
Phipps, Henry, 82, 102
Phipps Dispensary, 82
Phipps Psychiatric Clinic, 82, 102–106, 110
Photography, of surgical operations, 23–25
Phthalein, 113
Physiological Institute of Leipzig, 131
Physiology, 14, 38, 53, 64, 118, 137
  Howell's textbook on, 64
Plasma, 68, 169
Plastic surgery (see Surgery)
Poisoning, experiments on, 66–67
"Popsy" (see Welch, William H.)
Prayer, before operating, 22
Princeton, 16, 154
"Professor" (see Halsted, William S.)
Prostate glands, 111
Psychiatry, 103–106
  women in, 34
Public health, 175
Pyloroplasty, 158

R

Radium therapy, 23
Raynaud's disease, 24
Reed, Lowell J., 120, 205
Remsen, Ira, 1, 15, 62, 79, 113
Resident system, 43–48, 136–137, 155–156
  advantages of, 46–48, 131–132
  faults of, 48–49
Residents, 18–19, 131–132, 148
  in medicine, 44
  in pathology, 48
  in psychiatry, 103
  in surgery, 44–45, 85–86, 155–156
Rich, Arnold, 72, 211
Richardson, Edward H., 143
Rockefeller, John D., 82

Rockefeller, John D., Jr., 82
Rockefeller Foundation, 118–121, 164, 170–171, 173
　General Education Board, 172, 174–175
Rockefeller Institute, 24, 48, 80n., 119, 192
Rowland, Henry A., 1, 15
Rowntree, Leonard, 66, 113
Rubber gloves, 72, 130, 177
Russell, William W., 143

S

St. Agnes Hospital, 24, 144, 150
St. Joseph's Hospital, 145
San Antonio, Texas, 112–113
Sargent, Sir John Singer, 7
Saunders, W. B., Company, 134
School of Art as Related to Medicine, 134
Schwentker, Francis F., 108n., 211
Secondary Medical Center of Baltimore, 142, 145, 147–151
Sigerist, Henry E., 172, 175–176, 212
Singer, Charles, 175
Skin-grafting, 158
Smith, Frank R., 143
Smith, Winford, 210
Social service, 74–75
Society of Friends, 2–4
Sodium citrate, 68, 169
South Pacific, Hopkins Unit in, 202
Spalteholz, Werner, 131
S.P.C.A., 91–94, 97
Stone, Harvey B., 143
Sudhoff, Karl, 172–174
Suicide, from bichloride poisoning, 66
Sulfaguanidine, 193
Sulfas, 95, 169, 193
Surgeons, 21–23, 146
　brain, 184, 191
　demand for, 137
　genitourinary, 111, 117
　neuro-, 88, 98–101
　and private practice, 144–145
　women, 33–34
　in World War I, 115–117, 163–167

Surgery, 11–14, 21, 23, 29, 57, 63, 163, 210–211
　abdominal, 22
　animal, 91–98
　　course in, 88
　blood vessel, 20
　brain, 87, 96–101
　breast, 21, 158
　British, 175
　for children, 109–110
　experimental, 88
　eye, 63–64
　gall bladder, 161–162
　genitourinary, 51, 114, 117, 210
　goiter, 20
　　toxic, 159
　heart, 89–90
　hernia, 86
　for intestinal obstruction, 148
　and the layman, 96–97
　liver, 66
　minor, 34
　neuro-, 210
　operative, teaching of, 89
　plastic, 97, 148, 151
　residents in, 44–45, 85–86, 155–156
　scrubbing up for, 177
　stomach and intestinal, 65
　teaching of, 104–105
　thyroid, 158
　urological, 111–112
　war, 116, 165–167
Surgical instruments, 13, 87, 89, 111, 113
Sutures, blood vessel, 24–25
　nerve, 57
Syphilis, 20, 136

T

Takamini, J., 61
Taussig, Helen B., 108, 112
Te Linde, Richard, 211
Thayer, 49–50, 71, 143, 163, 167, 185–186
Thom, Helen Hopkins (great-grandniece of Johns), 5
Thomas, M. Carey, 30–32

Tiffany, Louis McLane, 35
Tissues, respect for, 21
Toronto University, 79
Tuberculosis, 20
  dispensary for, 82
Typhoid fever, 20, 135

U

Ulcer of the stomach, 158
Union Memorial Hospital, 153, 202
Union Protestant Infirmary, 144, 149–
  150, 153, 158
University of Chicago, 57, 80
University of Maryland, 35–36, 52,
  122, 144–145, 192
University of Pennsylvania, 7, 11, 21,
  138
University of Virginia, 51, 112
Uremic poisoning, 66
Urology, 221
    (*See also* Brady Urological In-
      stitute)

V

Vanderbilt University, 203
Venereal disease, 115
    (*See also* Syphilis)
Ventriculography, 100
Vertebral column, "slipped disk" of,
  100
Veterans, doctor, 204, 210
Vienna, 107
Vincent, George E., 173
Vital statistics, 119
Vitamins, 107, 120
Voegtlin, Carl, 61–62, 66
Von Pirquet, Clemens, 107

W

Walker, George, 167
War, and mental ills, 105–106
    (*See also* World War I; World
      War II)
Wards, 18, 153, 202
  free, 144, 148
  private, 143–144

Wards, rounds of, 19–20, 136
  teaching done on, 38
Washington (D. C.), 21, 175
Welch, William H. ("Popsy"), 1, 7–
  8, 10–14, 29–31, 36, 48, 51–56, 58,
  62, 69–72n., 79, 81–82, 84, 87, 89,
  102, 112–113, 118, 122, 131, 137,
  146, 206, 211, 214, 220–222
  description of, 11, 16–17
  and full time, 164, 190–191
  and S.P.C.A., 91–94
  and Welch Institute, 172–176, 191
Welch Institute of the History of
  Medicine, 172–176
Welch Memorial Library, 7, 172, 174
Whipple, George Hoyt, 71–72, 97
Whisky, "Hopkins Best," 3–4
Whitehall (Hopkins homestead), 3
Whitehorn, John Clare, 105
Williams, J. Whitridge, 36, 52, 71,
  122–127, 163, 200
Williams & Wilkins Company, 61
Wilmer, William Holland, 170–171
Wilmer Institute for Diseases of the
  Eye, 110, 170–171
Winternitz, Milton Charles, 71–72
Wolman, Samuel, 143
Wood, Gen. Leonard, 88
Woods, Alan, 171
World War I, 8, 53, 57, 79, 98, 114–
  117, 142, 152, 156, 183, 201–204
  Hopkins Unit in, 163–168
World War II, 183
  Hopkins Unit in, 202–203
  medical developments in, 168–169
Wyman, William, 28

X

X ray, 51–52, 71, 86–87, 97, 128, 163,
  210
  burns from, 129–130

Y

Yale University, 7, 9, 15, 107
Young, Hugh H., 51, 111–117, 139,
  146, 167, 193, 200, 210